A BANTAM PATHFINDER EDITION

THE NATURAL WORLD OF NORTH AMERICA

Between the Atlantic and Pacific Oceans, the tundras of Canada and the jungles of Central America, thousands of plants and animals have staked their claim. The diversity of the land provides the varied conditions for this incredible wildlife growth:

SEASHORES—built of skeleton corals, sandy beaches and rocky shores

MOUNTAINS—cone-shaped, dome-shaped, folded and faulted, from the alpine peaks of Mount Whitney to the worn, sloping Appalachians

GREAT PLAINS—the sea of grass that sweeps for more than 750 miles across the continent

DESERTS—burned, blown, eroded—endless miles of sand, hard-packed flatlands, and golden, shifting dunes

FORESTS—blanketing the East, lying astride the Pacific coastal ranges and the high Sierras, climbing the Rockies

This book includes concise descriptions of trees, flowers, insects, reptiles, birds, and mammals found in each environment.

Learn how wildlife adapts.

Learn to identify hundreds of plants and animals.

Judith Viorst writes regularly for Science Service. Among the many assignments that she has completed for them are two books: PROJECTS: SPACE, and, with Shirley Moore, THE WONDERFUL WORLD OF SCIENCE. Science Service is a non-profit institution for the popularization of science. Its many ambitious projects include the famous science fairs held throughout the country, the National Science Fair-International, and the Science Talent Search. Another service is the publication of the SCIENCE NEWS LETTER, which enables students and the general public to keep up with the latest information on developments in science. Mrs. Viorst is also the author of 150 SCIENCE EXPERIMENTS: STEP-BY-STEP, a Bantam Pathfinder Edition.

BANTAM PATHFINDER EDITIONS

provide the best in fiction and nonfiction in a wide variety of subject areas. They include novels by classic and contemporary writers; vivid, accurate histories and biographies; authoritative works in the sciences; collections of short stories, plays and poetry.

Bantam Pathfinder Editions are carefully selected and approved. They are durably bound, printed on specially selected high-quality paper, and presented in a new and handsome format.

THE NATURAL WORLD:

A Guide to North American Wildlife

BY JUDITH VIORST

BANTAM PATHFINDER EDITIONS

NEW YORK / TORONTO / LONDON

RLI: $\frac{\text{VLM 8.0}}{\text{IL 8.12}}$

THE NATURAL WORLD:
A GUIDE TO NORTH AMERICAN WILDLIFE
A Bantam Pathfinder Edition / published October 1965

Library of Congress Catalog Card Number: 65-24950

Published simultaneously in the United States and Canada.

Bantam Books are published by Bantam Books, Inc., a subsidiary of Grosset & Dunlap, Inc. Its trade-mark, consisting of the words "Bantam Books" and the portrayal of a bantam, is registered in the United States Patent Office and in other countries. Marca Registrada. Bantam Books, Inc., 271 Madison Avenue, New York, N. Y. 10016.

PRINTED IN THE UNITED STATES OF AMERICA

Preface

Forty-eight of the United States of North America form a contiguous land mass of great beauty and variety. Wave-washed shores, hushed forests and soaring mountains, vast stretches of grassy plain and shimmering desert—all can be found between Canada and Mexico "from sea to shining sea."

This book will take you through these regions and introduce you to the natural wonders to be discovered there. It provides detailed descriptions of more than 400 representatives of the animal kingdom—mammals, reptiles, insects, marine invertebrates, and birds. Some 140 members of the plant kingdom, including trees and shrubs, native grasses, desert and alpine wildflowers, and marine algae, are also described.

To give perspective to your observations of nature, the book begins with a chapter on the past. This chapter examines theories of Earth's origin and discusses the formation of the continents, the mountains, and the seas, and the development of life. It also offers an over-all view of the present look of the land that lies between the Atlantic and Pacific.

More than eighty photographs accompany the text, and the good-sized bibliography will enable you to pursue your favorite subjects in greater depth. We hope these descriptions will show you new aspects of the natural world, whether you are indeed climbing a mountain and beachcombing by the sea, or exploring it in your armchair through the pages of this book.

WATSON DAVIS, DIRECTOR
SCIENCE SERVICE

Acknowledgments

Many people helped in the preparation of this book. They guided me to source materials, they offered invaluable advice, and several of them painstakingly checked various sections of the manuscript. I would like to thank them here.

From Science Service: Watson Davis, Ann Ewing, Margit Friedrich, Marcia Nelson, Dorothy Schriver, and Barbara Tufty.

From the Smithsonian Institution: Sophia Burnham (Assistant Curator, Museum Service), Dr. Fenner A. Chace, Jr. (Senior Scientist, Department of Zoology), Dr. Doris M. Cochran (Curator, Division of Reptiles and Amphibians), Dr. Mason E. Hale, Jr. (Curator, Division of Cryptogams), Dr. Harold Robinson, Jr. (Associate Curator, Division of Cryptogams), Dr. Henry W. Setzer (Associate Curator, Division of Mammals), and Dr. Jason R. Swallen (Head Curator, Department of Botany).

From the U.S. Department of Agriculture: Dr. B. D. Burks, Dr. Reynold A. Dahms, and Philip B. Dowden.

From the U.S. Geological Survey: Dr. Raymond L. Nace and Dr. Frank C. Whitmore, Jr.

Also: Dr. John Aldrich (U.S. Department of the Interior), Howard Bray (Office of Senator Clinton P. Anderson), Esther Manion (National Geographic Society), Kenneth Pomeroy (American Forestry Association), and Milton Viorst (Husband Extraordinary).

JUDITH VIORST

Contents

THE NATURAL WORLD:

A Guide to North American Wildlife

Spiral nebula

Chapter 1

THROUGH THE PAST

LONG ago a planet was born in space. Great upheavals formed its continents and seas, and at some unknown point in time the boundary between nonlife and life was crossed.

You will be exploring a part of this planet, the continent of North America, as it stands today, with its varied land forms and its plant and animal life. Different as the mountains are from the seashores, the deserts from the forests, they share with each other and with the rest of the world a common history.

Part of this history remains in the realm of speculation and hypothesis, but much of it can be read in the ancient rocks. They reveal many of the literally earthshaking events of the planet and present before the eyes of the knowing observer the colorful and awesome panorama of evolution that leads from life's obscure beginnings to its present rich diversity.

Earth's Origins

There were no witnesses, somewhere between four and five billion years ago, to the birth of our planet. Early man created pretty myths to describe its origins, while the ancient philosophers attempted to explain the great event by applying their reasoning minds to the limited phenomena they could observe. But no real scientific explanation emerged until the eighteenth century, when German metaphysician Immanuel Kant and, later, French mathematician and astronomer Pierre Simon de Laplace presented their nebular hypothesis.

According to this hypothesis, a great cloud of gas, called a nebula, once rotated slowly out in space, extending in size at least as far as our solar system's outermost planet. Gradually, as its heat was dissipated by radiation, the nebula cooled, contracted, and spun faster. As the speed of rotation increased, so did the centrifugal force, which tends to cause an object to disintegrate. When the centrifugal force exceeded the gravitational force, which tends to hold an object together, the nebula dropped off rings of fiery gas. The central body of gas contracted to form the sun, while the rings broke up, gathered into spheres, and formed planets, several of which repeated the procedure of their mother nebula to produce satellites. In this hypothesis, which was widely accepted during the nineteenth century, the Earth was originally a gas, later cooling to a liquid and ultimately becoming solidified into its present form.

At the end of the nineteenth century two Americans, geologist Thomas Chamberlin and astronomer Forest Moulton, proposed the planetesimal hypothesis. In this version of the beginning of the world, the gravitational pull of a star raised high tides on the sun as it passed near, drawing out great bolts of gas which proceeded to revolve rapidly around the sun. Some of the gas condensed to liquid and then to solid particles called planetesimals. The planetesimals, which resembled meteorites, repeatedly collided until larger bodies—the planets—were formed. The earth, in this hypothesis, was built up by a process of accretion and was solid from the start.

Astronomer James Jeans and geophysicist Harold Jeffries, both Englishmen, offered a modification of the planetesimal hypothesis in the early part of the twentieth century. Their tidal hypothesis also assumed the close passage of a star which raised tides on the sun and pulled out a filament of solar gas. However, it said, this incandescent filament remained in a gaseous state during the time that it broke up and formed rotating spheres—the planets. It was only later that Earth cooled to a liquid and, finally, a solid state.

Scientists have pointed out flaws in all these versions of earth's origins and have proposed new hypotheses to modify or replace them. Prominent among the modern thinking on the subject is the protoplanet hypothesis of Carl von Weizsacker and Gerald Kuiper, which postulates a nebula made of gas and dust. This nebula, they say, had a diameter about the size of a light-year—some 186,000 miles per second multiplied by the number of seconds in a year (six million million miles). It moved very slowly at first, but later condensed and speeded up. As a result of rotation, the outer part of the nebula flattened into a thin disk in which swirled turbulent eddies of gas and dust particles. The friction of these different particles moving past each other slowed the rotation of the central mass, which became the sun, and made the outer parts move faster. (This accounts, as the nebular hypothesis did not, for the fact that the sun rotates far more slowly than most of the planets.) The gas-dust disk broke up into smaller clouds, called protoplanets, which were considerably larger than the planets of our solar system today. They gradually grew smaller, speeded up, and formed their satellites just as the original nebula did.

Some time after the formation of the protoplanets, the sun began to shine as a star. The pressure of radiation and the streams of particles shot off by the sun did away with most of the light gases of the inner planets, which is why Mercury, Venus, Earth, and Mars are rocky and metallic. The sun's radiation and particles had less effect on the more distant planets, and so Jupiter, Saturn, Uranus, Neptune, and Pluto are primarily gaseous.

It is unlikely that we will ever have positive knowledge of how the earth began. But the improvement of telescopes and photographic equipment, and the placing of instruments on the moon, may eventually bring us closer to the truth. Astronomers have already studied the life history of stars far, far out in space. Someday, when they can be studied at closer range from a moon observatory, we will get a more intimate look at the mysterious processes of creation in our universe.

The Land and the Sea

Over the course of thousands of centuries our probably once-molten earth whirled in its orbit, cooling slowly and slowly developing the features that now characterize it. The period of its infancy was undoubtedly one of furious upheaval, with continuous eruptions of burning lava cast up from the interior onto the cooling outer layers. After many false starts and collapses, a plastic mantle—perhaps made up of the mineral olivine—developed around the iron and nickel inner core, sealing in its tremendous heat and providing a base on which rests the earth's thin basalt surface crust. Granitic materials, continuing to burst upward from the core, gradually united and congealed on the heavier basalt underlayer, either as separate masses or as one huge granite platform which later broke up and moved apart to form the continents.

While the continents developed and froze in their proper places, water vapor and other gases rose from the interior and settled over the earth in massive cloud banks, shutting out the sun. Occasionally these clouds condensed into rain, but the falling waters were promptly boiled away by the hot surface. In time, however, the crust cooled below the boiling point of water. A monumental flood, lasting for centuries, turned earth's hollow places into ponds and lakes and rivers, and filled the ocean basins with about 20 percent of the water they hold today. New water, which may have been squeezed up through the basaltic basins as the earth's interior cooled and contracted, brought the oceans to their present levels many hundreds of thousands of years after the first rains fell.

According to one theory, the cooling of the earth continued and, near its core, contraction continued too. As it shrunk away from the outer crust, the crust wrinkled and folded, like the skin of an apple. These wrinkles and folds, occurring at weak places in the ocean basins and continental rock, formed the first mountains—some buried deep in the water, others rising high on the land. As soon as the mountains rose from the continents, the processes of erosion took over, loosening particles of sand and soil and rock to be washed into the sea by mountain streams. Dissolved minerals, including salt, were also carried seaward.

Inexorably the first mountains were worn away and the contours of the earth were simplified. Large areas of the flattened continents were covered by shallow seas, which deposited rich layers of sediment and reshaped the land. Then followed another upheaval in the earth's crust, accompanied by new mountain building and the recession of the seas.

The pattern of revolution and mountain building, uplifting of the continents and retreat of the waters, erosion and submergence, has occurred again and again in earth's history. Each time, it has left our planet altered. The features that we know today are not those the sun shone on a hundred million years ago, nor is it likely that they resemble those that will appear a hundred million years hence.

Life Comes to Earth

The conditions of the planet in its early phases were not hospitable to life. The seas lay empty and the bleak rocks bare. For perhaps as long as half its history the earth remained lifeless, but at last the process of evolution was set under way.

The theory of evolution was comprehensively formulated in the nineteenth century by the great British naturalist Charles Darwin. All life, said Darwin, is part of the same family. It has progressed from the simplest of living things to organisms of increasing complexity culminating, in recent times, with man. Every individual that has existed differs slightly from all others. In each generation those individuals whose differences are best suited for dealing with their environment are the ones that survive and reproduce, resulting in the continuation of the species. Evolution, then, involves a constant struggle for existence in which survival of the fittest is achieved through natural selection. As for the unfit—they perish.

There is a great deal of evidence to support Darwin's theory. The most compelling is the record left by fossils, remains of past plant and animal life preserved, for the most part, in layers of sedimentary rocks. Radioactive dating techniques have made it possible to determine the ages of these rocks, thus enabling geologists to place the fossil remains in their proper niches in time.

Beginning some 600 million years ago, the fossil records are abundant. But they display organisms that are relatively well developed and, therefore,

Cambrian submarine landscape (Paleozoic)

imply a vast previous time during which life initiated and embarked on its evolutionary path. The segment of earth history that includes these events is called Pre-Cambrian time. It began when the first rocks were formed and ended more than a half billion years ago.

Lost in these inconceivably distant years is the story of how life came into being. Perhaps, some scientists say, solar radiation and other forces acted upon elements present in our early atmosphere to produce proteins and amino acids—the two chemicals basic to every living thing. Somehow these chemicals eventually united, forming, in the sea, the first organism capable of reproducing itself.

There are no traces of these earliest life forms. All that has been verified so far are deposits of primitive algae and fungi to represent the plant kingdom, and the burrows and trails of wormlike animals. We can assume, however, that these developed from one-celled, soft-bodied, sea-dwelling organisms which were neither animal nor plant, but which served as the matrix for all succeeding life.

Three great geologic eras—the Paleozoic, which ended 225 million years ago, the Mesozoic, which ended 70 million years ago, and the Cenozoic, which has not yet come to a close—followed the ancient Pre-Cambrian time. Within this enormous span of years, backboneless animals and primitive plants gave way to more and more sophisticated forms. Nonvascular plants—without true leaves, stems, roots, or any mature mechanism for conducting food and water—yielded to modern flowers and grasses and trees. And from tiny sea-dwelling invertebrates evolved the entire animal kingdom that today occupies our lands, our waters and our skies.

The World of North America

Although mammals are the dominant life form on our planet, they have by no means excluded other

forms. In the forty-eight contiguous states of North America, the area of our exploration, the lowest as well as the highest creatures prevail. The great variety of life found between the Atlantic and Pacific Oceans,

Coal forest landscape (Mesozoic)

Canada and Mexico, reflects to a large extent the great variety of our landscape and climate.

Between New England and Florida, along the Atlantic shore, lies the low, flat Coastal Plain. In the

South it is 100 or more miles wide, but in the North it narrows and virtually disappears. At its ocean boundary, the Coastal Plain is bordered by beaches and marshes and swamps. At its western boundary lies the older, harder rock of the undulating and somewhat higher Piedmont country.

Westward still, the Piedmont gives way to the Appalachian Mountains. These worn, ancient ranges, shutting out the coastal regions from the interior, extend for more than 1600 miles from the St. Lawrence in Quebec all the way to central Alabama. They include the White and Green Mountains of New England, the Catskills of New York, Virginia's Blue Ridge Mountains, and the Great Smoky Mountains of North Carolina and Tennessee.

A vast forest blankets almost the entire eastern half of the country. In the North there are hardwoods, further South there are piney woods, and in southern Florida the lush trees of the tropics. These eastern forests climb the Appalachians and gradually subside beyond the Mississippi.

Forest yields to the tall grasses of the prairie, a region of fairly humid climate. The prairie grasses, in turn, merge into a semiarid region of short grasses, known as the Great Plains. The Great Plains reach from Canada to Mexico for more than 1600 miles. The sea of grass sweeps westward until halted abruptly by our second mighty mountain barricade, the Rockies.

Standing between 7000 and 14,000 feet high, this complex mountain chain looms from central New Mexico to Montana's Canadian border. The Continental Divide winds through the Rockies from North to South, separating the rivers that flow to the Atlantic from those that flow to the Pacific. A thick coniferous forest covers the Rocky Mountains. Below the timberline grow Engelmann spruce and Douglas fir, and in the lower zones, juniper and pinyon pine.

Beyond the Rockies lie the basins and plateaus of the arid southwestern deserts. These include the

Great Basin Desert of Utah and Nevada, the small Painted Desert of Arizona, and California's Sonoran and Mojave.

Further West the Cascade Range runs south from British Columbia to California for over 700 miles, paralleling the Pacific Coast 100 to 150 miles inland. The wall of mountains is continued by the Sierra Nevadas, which travels southeast for 400 miles to the Tehachapi Pass. Coniferous forests appear again in the Far West—one along the Cascade and Sierra ranges, another following the coast from western Alaska to central California.

The western boundary of the land is formed by the coastal ranges and the pounding shores of the Pacific Ocean.

Each of these regions has its own requirements for survival. The plants and animals we shall find there have met these requirements in a number of ingenious ways.

On the wave-washed coasts, marine invertebrates maintain their precarious perch by burrowing into sand, retreating into shells, or clinging onto rocks with suction cups of fleshy tissue. High on the mountaintops, where plants are perpetually threatened by raging winds, they have developed dwarfed, ground-hugging forms. The buffalo of the Great Plains wears a heavy winter coat to endure the punishing blizzards. Desert plants lie dormant, store water, or develop deep water-seeking taproots in their efforts to thrive in an arid land. And many forest creatures retreat into sleep to avoid the hardships of winter.

Virtually every corner of North America and, indeed, of the entire planet, is inhabited. No matter what conditions prevail, it seems that there is always some enterprising member of the plant or animal kingdom capable of adapting to them and making, of the most unlikely places, a home.

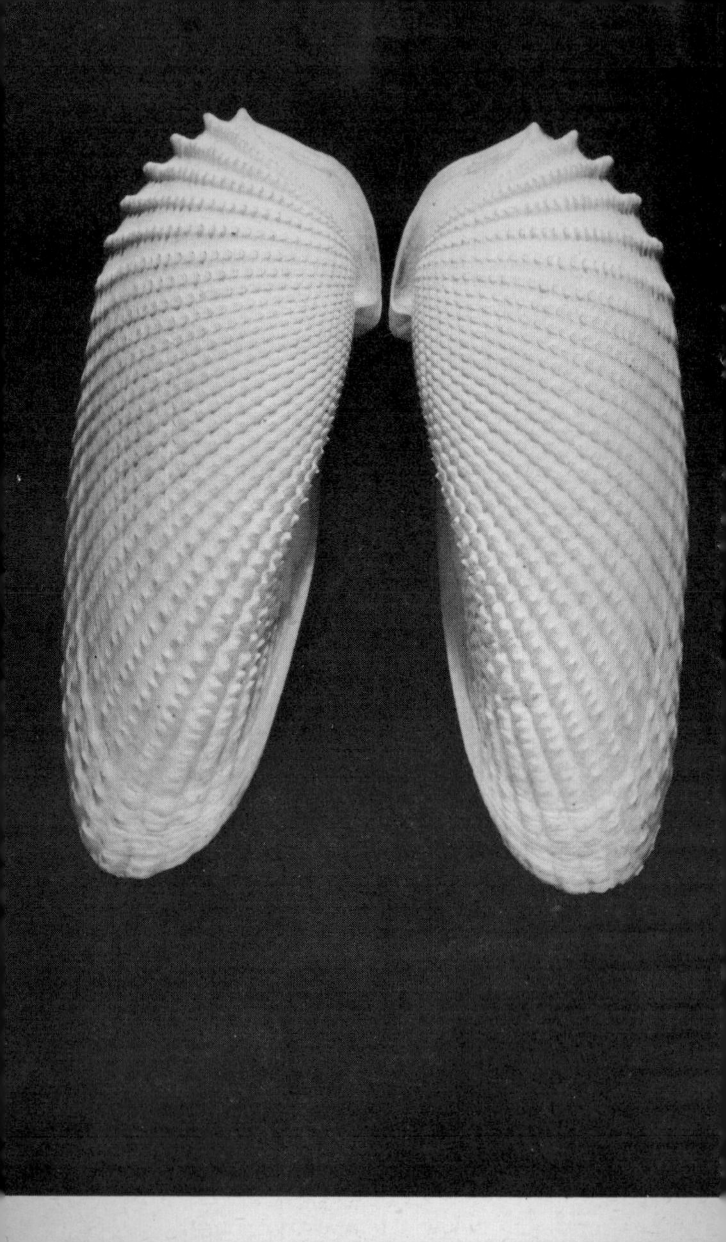

Angel wings

Chapter

2

ALONG THE SEASHORE

OUR PLANET Earth is more than 70 percent sea, about 330 million cubic miles of restless salty water. Where sea meets land a fascinating, unstable shore world is created, a world whose nature constantly alters as the tides ebb and flow.

Earth has, altogether, over a million miles of seacoast; 54,000 miles belong to continental United States alone. In our walk along the beaches of this continent we will be examining an area rich in plants and animals, some of which have remained nearly unchanged since they first came to life in the ancient Paleozoic seas.

Beaches

The shores of our seas may be protected coasts, sheltered from the violence of the surf, or exposed coasts, where the breakers pound relentlessly against the land. But sheltered or exposed, beaches are, basically, either coral, rock, or sand.

The sole coral coast of the United States is located in the Florida Keys, where the warm tropical waters rarely fall below a temperature of 70 degrees.

The colorful, gardenlike reefs are the work of stony corals, primarily colonial creatures that secrete lime, forming cuplike skeletons. Joined together in a variety of graceful architectural forms, the living corals grow outward and upward, multiplying by budding. Those near the bottom of the reef eventually die, leaving behind their hard lime shells to serve as a continuing foundation.

Rocky coasts often display handsome caves and arches, terraces and cliffs, sculptured by the endlessly hammering waves. Sandy beaches are composed of grains that began, thousands of centuries ago, as distant mountain rocks which were weathered, decayed, ground, and polished as wind and water carried them to the sea.

On some coasts the water eats away the rock at the rate of 15 to 30 feet a year. Elsewhere, during that same year, tons of sand are scooped from one beach and dumped upon another. The activity of the waves as they build, destroy, and rearrange is never-ending. And so the shapes of the shores change every minute of every day.

Tides

Twice a day the sea moves slowly up the beach and twice a day moves slowly back again. The gravitational pull of the moon (and, to a much lesser extent, of the sun) is responsible for these tides.

Once every 24 hours, as our planet turns on its axis, a given place on the earth directly faces the moon and the moon pulls the water away from the earth, causing a water bulge. Once every 24 hours that given place on the earth is directly opposite the moon and the moon pulls the earth away from the water. At these times the tide will be high. High tide occurs 50 minutes later each day because the moon, which circles the earth in the course of a month, has moved that much farther along its path.

When the moon is full or new, high tides are higher and low tides (which occur at regular intervals between the highs) are lower. At these times the sun and moon, lined up with each other and with the earth, exert their combined gravitational force upon our planet, producing what are called "spring" tides. The moon in its quarter phases exerts its pull at right angles to that of the sun. At these times the two bodies counteract each other, producing the sluggishly moving "neap" tides.

As the waters ebb and flow, the area between the high and low tides is alternately dried and flooded. To avoid desiccation when the sea recedes, the animals of sandy beaches become burrowers, hiding out in the depths of wet sand. At flood tide they come to the surface, or draw the needed water down into their subterranean homes by means of siphons or tubes.

The rock dwellers, unable to submerge into sand, are confronted not only with the dangers of drying but with the tearing and crushing force of the breakers. Snails retire into their shells, worms into calcareous tubes, when the tide is low. Other creatures seek the shelter of seaweeds or rocks. When the waves pound the rocks the limpet hangs on with a suction cup of fleshy tissue, the barnacle with its natural cement, the mussel with tough silken threads, and the seaweed with its rootlike organ. Boring clams and angel wings solve the problem by drilling holes into the rocks and moving into them.

The tides make the edge of the sea a hazardous habitat for shore life. And yet millions of plants and animals live here—digging, clinging, coating, drifting—stubbornly creating a place for themselves in this difficult, beautiful world.

Marine Algae

Sweep a nylon net through ocean water until the inside becomes coated with a slimy green and brown paste. In the brown material you will find (with the aid of a microscope) free-floating, one-celled algae called diatoms, which furnish nine-tenths of the food in the ocean and are so tiny that several million of them occupy a single quart of water. The microscope will reveal miniscule living organisms encased in a shell of shining silica, which can look like a pillbox, a bracelet, a wheel, or any number of other shapes. The two halves of the shell fit neatly into one another, and delicate patterns traced on the surface distinguish the various species. Diatoms begin the food chain of the sea; that is, they are eaten by the tiniest marine animals, which are in turn eaten by larger animals, and so on up to the fisherman. Without the presence of these microscopic plants, there would be little life in the water.

Seaweeds, a more familiar group of marine algae, are found along almost every shore, ranging in size from a tiny fraction of an inch to heights of over 100 feet. Unlike the higher plants, they have no true leaves or stems, and instead of roots, which serve as food suppliers, they have root-like structures called holdfasts, which serve merely to anchor them. Seaweeds are traditionally divided into four categories—the blue-greens, the greens, the browns, and the reds.

The so-called blue-green algae are not invariably blue-green but may be purple, brown, or pink instead. One microscopic member of this group, in fact, gives the Red Sea its red shade. These minute plants form a velvety fuzz on boat bottoms, or appear as slimy or scummy spots on mud and rocks. They are often encased in gelatinous sheaths, which guard them from extremes of heat and cold. On both the Atlantic and Pacific coasts you will encounter mermaid's hair (*Lyngbya*), composed of separate strands matted together. Use a strong hand lens or microscope to see the individual filaments, which are long, thick, and curled.

Green algae are best found on warm shores, thriving in the shallows. Unlike the reds and the browns, which are almost exclusively marine plants, these seaweeds abound in fresh as well as salt water. They range in color from pale greens to rich dark-green shades.

Largest of the green algae is the bright sea lettuce

Diatoms (greatly magnified)

(*Ulva*), which grows up to 3 feet long. True to its name, it often takes the form of a broad, leaflike sheet, although sometimes it is ribbonlike. Look for sea lettuce attached to rocks in shallow waters.

Sponge seaweed (*Codium*) is a branching plant with a dense covering of fine filaments that give it a soft, spongy texture. Among the most common of the green seaweeds, *Codium* can be found along the coasts of the southern Atlantic, the Gulf, and the Pacific.

You can see the feathery branching stalks of the sea moss (*Bryopsis*) along the entire Atlantic and Pacific, where it grows in tufts on rocks and piers at the low-water mark. Between 2 and 8 inches tall, the sea moss is a dark but vivid green.

Piers and boat bottoms house a common green algae named *Enteromorpha*. While some species are inflated and twisted, others have long, slender fronds bearing a resemblance to hair or grass.

Two tropical green seaweeds can be seen along the Florida coasts. Mermaid's cup (*Acetabularia*) consists of one great cell which has a mushroom shape and a gray-green color. The deep-green merman's shaving brush (*Penicillus*) is well-designed for lathering whiskers, with a short, thick, stemlike structure topped by a spreading tuft of soft filaments.

The brown seaweeds form great beds along the shores, displaying a variety of shapes from hairlike filaments to treelike structures. Thick, tough, and leathery, the brown algae contain a large amount of algin, a gelatinous substance that can easily absorb or lose water without being damaged. Thus they are ideally equipped for living where the tides ebb and flow.

The famous gulfweed (*Sargassum*) can be seen cast up on the beach or floating in the warmer waters of the Atlantic and Pacific. While most seaweeds are originally attached to rocks or other solid surfaces, the three-foot-long gulfweed grows in large drifting masses on the ocean. (Dense, slow-moving rafts of this plant form the buoyant vegetation of the At-

Sea colander

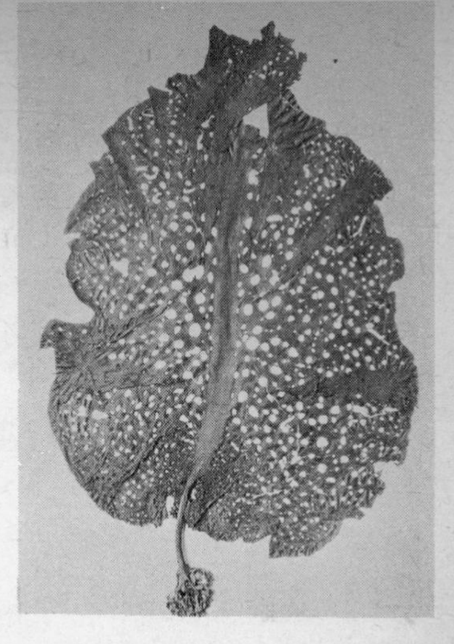

lantic's Sargasso Sea.) Gulfweeds are kept afloat by gas-filled, berry-sized swellings called air bladders. These are located on the weed's central stalk, which resembles a stem, or on its blades, which extend from the stalk in leaflike fashion.

The common rockweed (*Fucus*) also has air bladders to serve as buoys. This yellow-brown plant of the cool rock shores stands as high as 7 feet on protected beaches but grows only a few inches tall where the waves are fierce. Swaying gracefully, forests of rubbery *Fucus* dance in the waters of the incoming tide. When the ocean recedes, however, the seaweeds sag, forming a thick, matted drapery on the rocks. Among the rockweeds are the tall and slender knotted wrack, found where the shore is moderately protected; the forked wrack, a much shorter plant with flat, tapering fronds, present on unprotected shores; and the spiral wrack, a low, orange-brown weed with sturdy fronds which dwells on the upper shore untouched by the sea during most of its life.

The brown kelps thrive in the northern waters, growing from the low-tide mark out into the sea. Off the shores of the West Coast they reach lengths of over 100 feet, their tough holdfasts clutching the bottom, their air bladders holding them aloft. If you are on the Pacific shore, look for the sea palm (*Postelsia*), which clings to the rocky shores where the surf is rough. This unusual plant has a distinctly palmy appearance, with fronds drooping from the top of a flexible stalk 12 to 18 inches high. Other aptly named kelps are the sea colander (*Agarum*), whose wide fronds are perforated from top to bottom, and the horsetail kelp (*Laminaria*), which displays satiny brown ribbons waving from a common base.

Red algae frequently appear in the lower tidal pools of rocky beaches, where a depression or sealed-off corner of rock holds sea water. Along with the browns, they make up the major portion of the seaweeds. Included in the red algae group are Irish moss, laver, *Dasya*, and *Corallina*.

Irish moss (*Chondrus*) lies at the low-tide line in a dense mat of yellow-green, purple-green, or deep purple, often with a blue iridescence. Thick, stubby stalks, which look as if they had been hacked off at the ends, branch from a central "stem."

A cord of interwoven strands holds the purple laver (*Porphyra*) to its place on the rocks. Dried by the sun, the thin, lettucelike fronds of the laver become brittle, but the waters of the flood tide return them to their natural elastic state.

Graceful, thin, and hairy, the branches of the delicate *Dasya* flutter from a narrow central stalk which is anywhere from 6 inches to 3 feet long. Look for these purply-red or brownish-orange algae among the rocks on protected shores along both the Atlantic and Pacific coasts.

Corallines are among the most beautiful of all the seaweeds. Many species have a delicate fernlike appearance, with symmetrical branching; others are simply pink encrusting sheets. When found alive in rock pools or below low-tide mark, corallines are pink-purple or gray-green. Cast up on the beach and bleached by the sun, they turn pure white. Corallines have a limy crust and fronds that are rigid and flat.

Their lime-depositing ability contributes to the building up of coral reefs.

Marine algae are not the only plant forms seen on a seashore walk. There are a variety of dune shrubs and flowers, grasses and trees, which have learned to contend with wind, salt spray, and drought, developing adaptations like those of desert plants. There are the unmistakable mangrove trees, anchored in the mud or coral gravel of southern beaches by a tangle of buttress roots that prop up the trunk against the pressures of waves and wind. But the true plant of the seashore is the seaweed, which commands attention whether alive or dead, and proclaims by its presence that you are indeed at the ocean's edge.

Marine Invertebrates

In most geographical regions the vertebrates dominate the scene because they include all the higher forms of animal life. But down by the seashore it is the invertebrates we must examine most closely, for this is their domain.

The single-celled animals belong to the phylum Protozoa; multicelled animals are divided among all the other phyla of the animal kingdom. The first to look at are the sponges, which belong to the phylum Porifera, a name meaning "pore animal."

The microscopic pores referred to pierce the body wall of the sponge in countless numbers, and through them water is sucked into the tissues. The sponge strains out for its dinner the minute plants and animals present in the moving stream, expelling the water through a large hole at the top. Although sponges do not move from place to place, they are not at all lazy. It has been estimated that a good-sized sponge filters perhaps several hundred gallons of water in the course of 24 hours.

The familiar soft bath sponge, whose skeleton is composed of an organic material called spongin, is only one representative of this phylum. Other sponges are permeated with hard needlelike particles (spicules) or combine spicules and organic fibers.

The simplest are the lime sponges, supported by scattered spicules of lime. Single or colonial, they grow as inconspicuous "urns" or tubes, white, yellow, or gray in color, ⅛ inch to 5 inches in length. Included in this group are shore sponges of the genus *Leucosolenia,* found on rocky beaches near low-tide mark. These colonial creatures appear as little vertical tubes connected by little horizontal tubes. The purse sponge (*Grantia*) looks like a bag or purse.

Finger-shaped sponges are commonly found washed up on the beach. The redbeard sponge (*Microciona*) grows as a bright-red incrustation on shells and stones, sending up an erect mass of branching appendages. The gruesomely named deadman's fingers (*Chalina*) is a sickly white, yellow, or gray.

The usually pale-green bread crumb sponge (*Halichondria*) resembles its name, with a fairly smooth surface marked by miniature "volcanoes." Where the waves smash into the beach, this sponge is as thin as a sheet of paper. But back in the shelter of the tidal pool it forms a thick springy carpet.

Two particularly interesting sponges are the loggerhead (*Spheciospongia*) and the yellow boring sponge (*Cliona*). The cake-shaped loggerhead, a black massive creature of the Florida Keys, serves as a home for thousands upon thousands of sea dwellers, including pistol shrimp, crabs, and worms. *Cliona* is

Redbeard sponge

Star coral

considerably less sociable. It spreads itself over the shells of marine animals and gradually destroys them by puncturing their shells with a host of tiny holes.

Each member of the phylum Coelenterata is, basically, a hollow tube terminating at one end with a mouth surrounded by tentacles armed with "sting cells," nematocysts. There are, of course, many intriguing variations on this basic theme, resulting in such diversified creatures as corals, sea anemones, jellyfish, and hydroids.

The usually colonial corals may be soft, horny, or stony. Soft corals have only scattered spicules to stiffen the body and are often fleshy and flabby. Horny corals are supported by a material called gorgonin, which makes them both flexible and tough. Among the gorgonians are decorative plantlike growths in brilliant reds and purples, oranges and yellows, with whiplike (the sea whips) or lacy (the sea fans) "branches."

The true or stony corals, which include the reef-builders, secrete little limy cups. There are various star corals, hemispherical masses covered with star-shaped pits. There are various brain corals, whose convoluted surface makes the name strikingly apt.

And there is the staghorn coral (*Acropora*) growing in candelabra-shaped colonies.

The coral's closest relation is the sea anemone, an utterly flowerlike creature. At one end a flat disk attaches the anemone's upright stem of a body to a rock. At the other end, tentacles wave in the water like petals in a breeze.

Sea anemones

Best known of the anemones is *Metridium*, the plumose anemone. Found below low-tide mark, it has hundreds and hundreds of feathery tentacles in white, pink, orange, or brown, with a column of matching shade. The dahlia anemone (*Tealia*) may be bright red or pink, with short, blunt tentacles. Some anemones wear gay orange or yellow stripes. Others live on the back of hermit crabs, or have a green color because green algae dwell within their tissues.

The jellyfish has been described as an upside-down anemone, for instead of raising its tentacles skyward, it trails them from a central, umbrella-shaped disk. The moon jelly (*Aurelia*) is the most common and most widely distributed, with a transparent body, numerous short tentacles fluttering from a 6-to-10-inch disk, and 4 large horseshoe-shaped organs, often violet or pink, appearing near the center. A frequent companion of the moon jelly is *Cyanea,* the red or arctic jellyfish. This big creature grows up to 8 feet across, with tentacles 200 feet long, but the ones you are likely to encounter along the New England coast will probably be one-footers with tentacles under 75 feet.

Everyone is familiar with the reputation of the Portuguese man-of-war (*Physalia*), whose sting can cause serious damage or death to unwary swimmers. Its top section is a gas-filled, pear-shaped "float" colored purple, pink, red, or bright blue, with an iridescent crest above and streaming tentacles—40 to 60 feet long—hanging below. The man-of-war is, actually, a colonial organism, with some jellyfish and some hydroid components.

Hydroids reproduce by alternation of generations; that is, small, free-swimming jellyfish (medusae) produce an attached, plantlike generation (polyps) which in turn produce jellyfish, and so on. You will recognize hydroids in their plantlike state as a branching colony, with cups growing on the branches and tentacles lodged in the cups. Look for *Obelia,* found on almost every shore. Some species appear as deli-

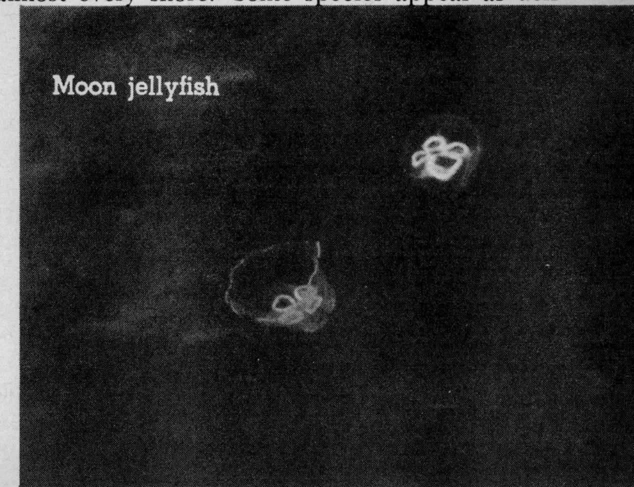
Moon jellyfish

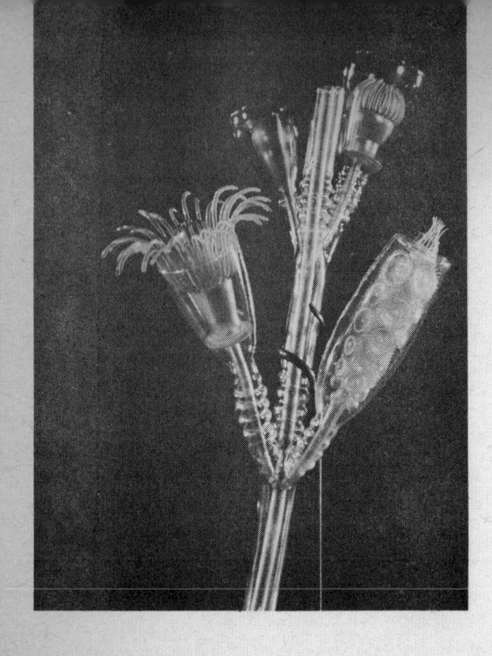

Obelia (glass model)

cate white sprays, 1 or 2 inches high, attached to rocks or seaweed. Other species, yellow in color and 8 to 12 inches long, may be seen in shallow waters below low-tide mark.

The gelatinous comb jellies, which closely resemble true jellyfish, are, nevertheless, members of a separate phylum—Ctenophora. Eight rows of fringed, comblike plates radiating across the surface of their body propel these jellies through the water and give them their name. A well-known form is the pretty 6-inch-long Venus girdle (*Folia*), a flat, ribbonlike creature of the Atlantic coast whose transparent body is delicately tinged with yellow and bordered with rainbow hues.

You will encounter several varieties of marine worms on your seashore walk. In tide pools or among the seaweeds and rocks look for the thin, flattened, soft-bodied flatworm (phylum Platyhelminthes), shaped like a leaf with a head at one end and a frill-encircled mouth in the middle of its underside. Some flatworms come in vivid shades and striking stripes. But even those that are drab in color can brighten dramatically after a meal, for their thin skins turn pink, purple, or orange when they eat foods of these shades.

In mud and sand and under rocks dwells the ribbon worm (phylum Nemertea), which may be cylindrical or flat, pale or vivid, and often handsomely patterned. Usually only a few inches long, it occasionally exceeds 30 yards in some forms. A distinguishing feature of the ribbon worm is its proboscis, a long, sheathed, frequently spine-tipped tube that can be discharged from the front end of the body to injure and entangle prey.

Segmented worms (phylum Annelida) are more advanced than the other two phyla. External rings,

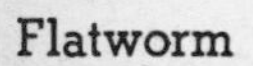
Flatworm

or segments, serve to identify these worms, which include an interesting and varied group of marine representatives. There is the stout clam worm (*Nereis*), which sometimes reaches lengths of 18 inches and displays brilliant iridescence when the sun shines on its green-blue or orange-red-tinged body. There is the sea mouse (*Aphrodite*), approximately the size and shape of its rodent namesake, covered with long gray hair. A pile of sandy casts beside the mouth of an underground burrow will tell you the lugworm (*Arenicola*) is near, and a U-shaped underground tube of tough leathery skin is the sign of the parchment worm (*Chaetopterus*).

Sometimes a stone or seaweed picked up at the edge of the sea will bear a hard, lacy crust that is white, yellow, or red. If you look at this lace work under a hand lens you may see colonies of beautifully formed, closely grouped chambers, each with a trap door that eventually opens to reveal a tiny crown of golden tentacles. These are the moss animals of the phylum Bryozoa. Some species grow as fluffy, tree-like colonies with tiny spiral branches; still others have a gelatinous texture.

Lamp shells (phylum Brachiopoda) may be found attached to rocks, usually by a muscular stalk. These exclusively marine animals have a bivalve shell that looks roughly like that of a mollusk, but the creature within is actually closely related to the bryozoans.

All members of the phylum Echinodermata, a name meaning "spiny-skinned," have skeletons composed of calcareous plates with projecting spines imbedded in the skin. A five-pronged star structure is the basic plan for these ancient marine invertebrates which include, in addition to stalked sea lilies, four common seashore groups: brittle and basket stars, sea

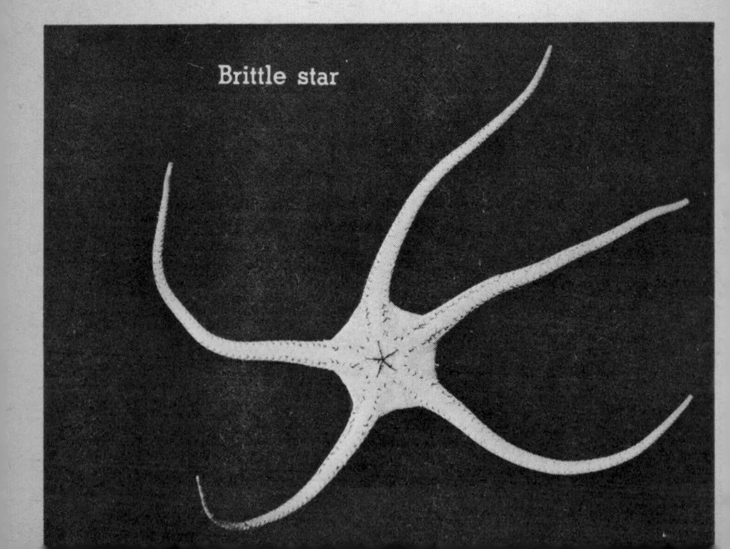
Brittle star

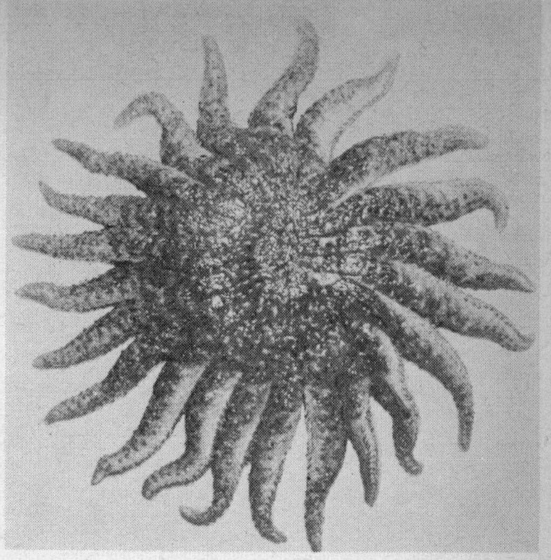

Pycnopodia, starfish

stars (starfish), sea urchins and sand dollars, and sea cucumbers.

The first two groups are made up of a central disk from which radiate, generally, five arms or rays. (This number may vary considerably, however.) The brittle stars have long serpentine rays, while those of the basket stars branch and rebranch, forming a tangled mass.

Among the sea stars of the Atlantic coast are the common starfish (*Asterias*), which comes in a variety of shades; the yellow pentagonal mud star (*Ctenodiscus*); the blood-red or yellow blood sea star (*Henricia*); the common, or spiny, sun star (*Crossaster*), a 10- or 12-rayed scarlet creature banded with crimson, pink, or white; the purple sun star (*Solaster*), red-violet in color with 7 to 13 rays; the sharp-rayed, symmetrical sand star (*Astropecten*); and the brilliantly colored giant starfish (*Oreaster*), 16 to 20 inches across, with thick rays and a heavy body. On the West Coast are the red or orange large sea bat (*Patiria*), named for its webbed rays; the sleek, purple-skinned leather star (*Dermasterias*), marked with red and turned up at the tips;

Sea urchins

and the pink-and-purple many-rayed sun star (*Pycnopodia*), with up to 24 arms and a spread of more than 24 inches. Also present in the West are *Henricia, Solaster* and *Astropecten.*

The typical sea star has a roughened, flattened body with suckers on the undersides of its arms and a mouth on the underside of its disk. A perforated plate called a madreporite, often mistaken for an eye, is located on the top side near the center. Sea water passes through the plate and into body canals, eventually entering little tube feet that terminate in the suckers. When water is withdrawn a powerful suction is created, enabling the starfish to move from place to place, cling to a wave-pounded rock, and pry open the stubborn shell of an oyster. This water-vascular system is characteristic of all echinoderms.

If you encounter a starfish with some arms smaller than others, you are probably seeing regeneration in progress. Starfish can grow new rays the way we grow new fingernails, and even can regrow a whole new body from a single ray if some of the central disk is attached to it. Another unusual starfish characteristic is its method of eating. Using its suction power to open an oyster shell, the starfish turns its stomach inside out through its mouth, pours digestive juices over the soft part of the victim, and devours the oyster right in its own shell.

Sea urchins and sand dollars bear no resemblance to starfish. Globular or oval, a rigid shell called a test encloses the body, and spines protrude from it. The typical five-ray design of the echinoderm can be seen on the shell's surface, however, identifying urchins and dollars as members of this phylum.

Sea urchins may be green, red, purple, or black. They range in diameter from 1½ to 10 inches and have a dense covering of movable spines, sometimes short and delicate, sometimes long and fierce. Five double rows of tube feet appear among the spines. Look for these rounded, prickly sea creatures on the sides and undersurfaces of rocks and coral reefs.

Sand dollars (also called sea biscuits) look like flattened sea urchins, with numerous small spines that give a velvety quality to the shell. The ray design appears as a five-petaled flower. These echinoderms live partly embedded in the soft sand or mud of the ocean, but you will find their shells cast up on the beach.

The final group of shore echinoderms is composed of sea cucumbers, shaped like the vegetable and colored red-brown, black, beige, or white. A mouth ringed with tentacles appears at one end, and in some species five tracts of tube feet extend down the length of the body. Tiny calcareous plates are scattered throughout the sea cucumber's leathery skin. Lengths range from just a couple of inches to a foot and a half. Most species live at the low-tide mark, attached to rocks by their little tube feet, but there are also

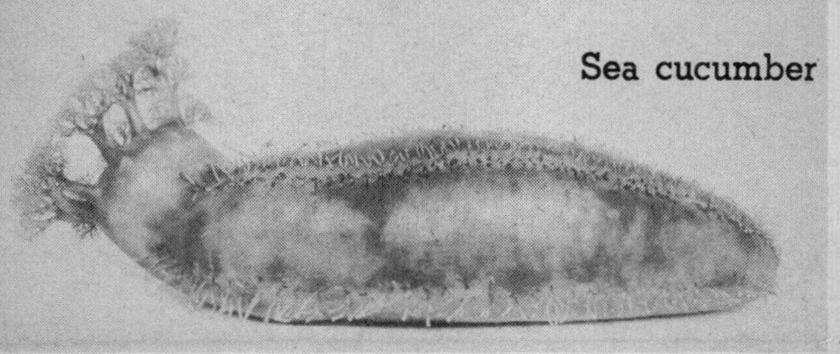
Sea cucumber

pale, wormlike types that burrow in the mud and sand.

The phylum Arthropoda (the joint-footed animals) has five times as many species as all other animal phyla combined. It includes the now-extinct trilobites and eurypterids of Paleozoic times, as well as the most highly developed of the invertebrates. Arthropods wear hard external skeletons which are periodically shed and replaced, and have segmented bodies from which paired, jointed appendages extend. Virtually all marine arthropods are crustaceans, among them beach fleas, barnacles, lobsters, shrimps, and crabs.

The tiny beach flea, also known as the sand hopper, may be found both on the dry beaches and in the sand and mud of shallow waters. Using its tail and rear legs, it can spring considerable distances into the air.

Barnacles, sturdy and abundant, are chiefly of two kinds—the squat, acorn-shaped rock or acorn barnacle (*Balanus*) and the gooseneck barnacle (*Lepas*), which has a long, flexible, leathery stalk. Firmly attached to rocks, driftwood, and boat bottoms, the adult barnacle hangs with its head down, in permanent residence. It feeds by trailing its feathery feet through the water in search of food, then brushing the food into its mouth.

The lobster on your dinner plate is bright red, but at the seashore, alive and uncooked, it is usually

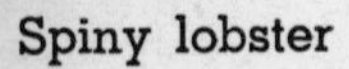

Spiny lobster

greenish. Like shrimps and crabs, its head and thorax are fused and covered with a hard shell called a carapace. The common American lobster (*Homarus*), found in submerged rocky crevices on the Atlantic coast, is equipped with two large and powerful pincer claws filled with tasty meat. The spiny lobster (*Panulirus*) of the Pacific coast is guarded by a coat of needle-sharp spines and has, instead of pincers, a pair of long legs.

In tide pools you may capture a broken-back shrimp (*Hippolyte, Spirontocaris*), a tiny, translucent creature whose beating heart and other internal activities can be observed, under a hand lens, like the moving works of a plastic clock. This pretty crustacean sprints backward by a sudden flexing of the tail, giving its body the strange appearance that justifies its name. The sand-colored sand shrimp (*Crago*) is more likely to be felt than seen, as it glides swiftly over your bare feet at the ocean's edge. And the dainty pistol shrimp (*Crangon, Synalpheus*) may never be seen or felt, but its presence will be made known by the snapping of its big claw, which punctuates the air with shotlike sounds.

Crabs have two well-developed eyes set on movable stalks, a segmented tail folded firmly under the body, and a sideways way of running. Among their

Blue crab

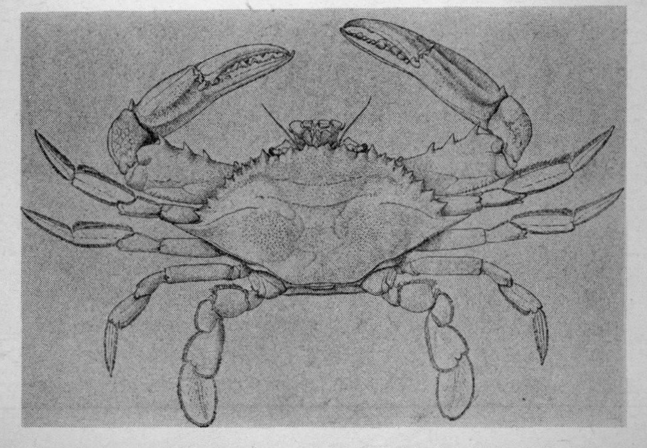

numerous representatives are hermit crabs, fiddler crabs, ghost crabs, spider crabs, and various swimming crabs.

The hermit crab (*Pagurus*) has a soft, curved abdomen and a hooklike tail. It backs itself into an empty mollusk shell and retreats inside it, trading in the borrowed shell for larger and larger models as it grows.

The male fiddler crab (*Uca*) has one great claw resembling a violin, and one tiny claw resembling a bow. During mating season, when the fiddler waves the big claw, perhaps in a flirtatious display, the motions give the impression of a virtuoso performance.

Fiddler crabs are burrowing crustaceans of the upper beach, and so are the ghost or sand crabs (*Ocypode*). The pale protective coloring of the ghost crab is so successful that the creature seems capable of vanishing from sight before your eyes.

The slow-moving, pear-shaped common spider crab (*Libinia*), narrow and pointed in front, harbors a growth of tiny animals and plants on its carapace. Its long, skinny legs have a spidery appearance.

Not all crabs are able to swim, but among those that can are the blue crab (*Callinectes*) and the lady or calico crab (*Ovalipes*). In both, the last pair of legs have a paddle shape and serve as oars.

As you look for crabs along the Atlantic shore, you will probably come across the king or horseshoe crab (*Limulus*) in the shallow waters of sheltered beaches below the low-tide mark. This strange East Coast creature, often called a "living fossil," is neither crab nor crustacean, but belongs to a different class of arthropods. You will recognize it by the large horseshoe-shaped shell and long, sharp spike of a tail.

The animals of the great phylum Mollusca are, typically, soft-bodied creatures with an outer skin or mantle that secretes a calcareous protective covering—the shell. They are divided into five groups.

First and most primitive is the chiton, an oval-shaped creature with eight overlapping plates forming a shell across the back. It lives on the open coast,

Squid

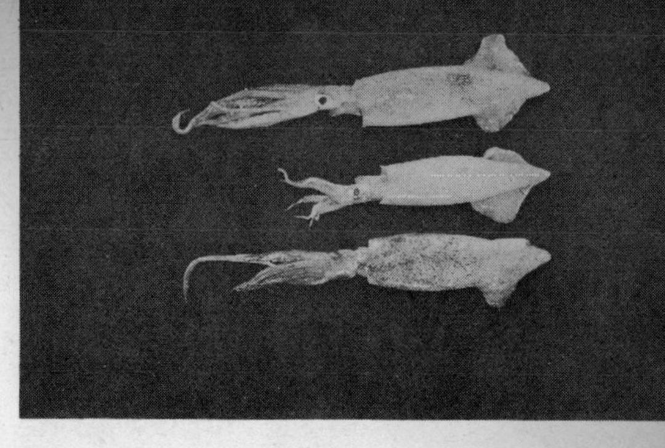

frequently attached to a rock by its large, muscular foot. In another group is the carrot-shaped tusk or tooth shell, 1 to 5 inches long, with a one-piece calcareous shell open at both ends. This mollusk lives in a head-down position in sand or sandy mud. The squid and its relatives comprise a third group, characterized by big heads, big eyes, and eight to ten tentacles. Some have an outside shell; some have an inside shell; some have no shell at all in their adult stage. The last two groups are the gastropods and pelecypods, producers of the beautiful, infinitely varied seashells found on almost every ocean shore. For beachcombers like us, they are the most significant of the mollusks.

The gastropods or sea snails are (almost entirely) univalves, animals with a single shell, coiled in spiral fashion. The name *gastropod* means "belly-footed"

Limpets

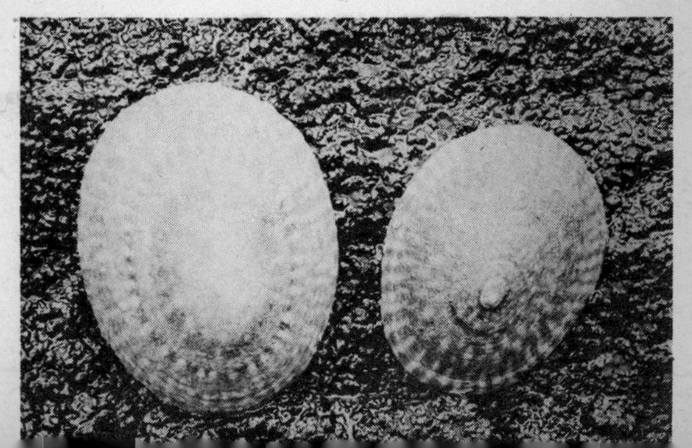

Abalone

and refers to the animal's broad foot, located in the stomach region and used for holding or gliding about. There is a distinct head area with eyes, feelers (tentacles), and a mouth equipped with a ribbon of tiny teeth (the radula). There is also a horny shield, called an operculum, which covers the opening of the shell when the mollusk withdraws.

A limpet is a gastropod whose larval spiral shell later develops into a flattened, conical one up to 4 inches long, brown or gray or blue in color. Some limpets wear a hole at the peak of the cone; some distinctly resemble Chinese coolie hats. The limpet's muscular foot hugs rock surfaces with a powerful grip. It requires a strong hand wielding a strong knife to separate this snail from its rock.

Look for abalones (all of the genus *Haliotis*) in the waters of our Pacific coast, where they cling fiercely, like limpets, to rocks. Their saucer-shaped 4-to-12-inch shells, punctured with holes to allow the passage of water, are rough and dark on the outside but have a pearly iridescence within.

Many species of top shells, noted for their pretty, pearly linings, are found on our shores. Ranging in

Moon shells

size from ½ to 4 inches, they bear a resemblance to the spinning top for which they were named.

The moon snail is an extremely carnivorous gastropod whose round, plump shell is barely able to house the oversized muscular foot with which it smothers prey. You may come across its egg case, called a "sand collar," as you walk along the shore. This unusual cape- or collar-shaped object is composed of a gelatinous ribbon of moon snail eggs thoroughly impregnated with sand grains.

The ½-to-1-inch periwinkle (mostly of the genus *Littorina*) is a dingy snail, often spotted or mottled. You will find its coiled shell, fat and round at the open end, on most shores, particularly among the seaweeds of rocky beaches.

In tropical water live the big, handsome conches, whose shells you have undoubtedly seen decorating someone's mantle or serving as a doorstop. Another good-sized gastropod is the whelk, 3 to 16 inches long and usually pear-shaped, with a pointed spire and a large body whorl. Both are carnivorous.

Cowries have highly polished and frequently

Conchs

bright-colored shells with an oval shape instead of the typical gastropod spiral. Look for the pretty shells of these tropical creatures along our warmer shores.

Murex snails live in fairly deep water, but you will find their shells cast up on the beaches. These heavy warm-shore shells are distinctively ridged and frequently spiny.

The sea hare, whose thin shell is hidden by the folds of its mantle, is a link between the shelled snails and the sea slugs, which have no shell at all. Named for the ear-shaped organs that sit on its head, the yellowish or greenish sea hare can grow as long as 15 inches and as heavy as 15 pounds. It emits a cloud of purple fluid when disturbed.

The shell-less sea slugs are very dashing-looking

Cowry

creatures. They have plumes or tufts along the back, and come in any number of vivid shades. Lengths range from under an inch to several inches.

The pelecypods or clams are bivalves—mollusks with two shells that are joined at a hinge. A bivalve has no head, but is equipped with a wedge-shaped foot for digging and, usually, two siphons—one to take in water (carrying food and oxygen), the other to expel water (carrying wastes). Many of the shells you find on the beach are one section of the original two-part pelecypod shell.

Among the pelecypods are nut clams, small in size, iridescent within, present on both coasts; mussels, attached to rocks and pilings by a tough thread (the byssus) secreted by a gland in the foot; and the delicate, pearly jingle shells (*Anomia*), light and thin, and almost transparent. The burrowing angel wings are also thin and delicate. When the two halves of their ridged shell are set side by side, they look (very

Murex

delightfully) like their namesake. Less attractive by far are the shipworms, long and wormlike with a greatly reduced shell. These mollusks bore into wharves and ship bottoms, causing great destruction.

In warmer waters you will find oysters, firmly and permanently cemented to rocks or to the shell of older oysters. The shape of the shell is irregular and the two valves are of different sizes.

Sea slug

The scallop is distinguished by rows of tiny bright eyes along the edge of the mantle. Its attractive fan-shaped shell, scalloped at the edge and fluted across the surface, has "ears" or "wings," unequal in size, projecting from each side of the hinge. Scallops range in size from 1 inch to 6 inches or more.

There are many varieties of burrowing clams, which dig into muddy or sandy bottoms (and sometimes into wood or rock). These include four genera of razor clams, elongated and skinny, with a shell that resembles a straight razor; the dull-white, oval-shaped soft shells (*Mya*), found in shallow mud flats; and the quahogs (*Mercenaria*) of the Atlantic coast, whose purple and white interior was used by the coastal Indians to make wampum.

One more group of marine invertebrates remains. These belong to the phylum Chordata and are generally obscured by more showy members of the phylum—like fishes, dinosaurs, and the human race. Almost all chordates are vertebrates, animals with backbones. But a few of the lower chordates, such as sea squirts and lancelets, have only a notochord. The notochord is a stiff rod that gives skeletal support to the body. In sea squirts it appears only in the larval stage; in lancelets it remains throughout life.

The sea squirt, which may be solitary or colonial, can be found from the intertidal zone to the deep ocean. Some resemble spongy grapes, others look like potatoes, still others have the size and velvety texture of a ripe peach. The sea squirt displays two spoutlike openings, one on the top, the other at the side, which take in and expel water. On its bottom (which is really its head region) the sea squirt is permanently attached to an object or buried in the ocean floor. A tough outer covering of cellulose, called a tunic, gives this animal its other common name—the tunicate. Colors range from white to jet, with many pretty shades in between.

Look for the lancelet buried in wet sand with only its front end exposed. Its translucent body is slim and flattened and comes to a point at each end. The chordate has great interest for scientists, because its notochord, appearing in adulthood as well as infancy, heralds the coming of the backbone, present in all the higher animals.

Shore Birds

Birds of many kinds live along the shores, seeking a seafood dinner by running up and down the beach, digging into the sand, fishing at the water's edge, or diving straight into the sea. Here are just a few of the American shore birds, represented by oystercatchers, sandpipers and their relatives, plovers and their relatives, terns, and gulls.

The American oystercatcher is a stout, black-and-white, crow-sized bird, whose dark head is dramatically set off by a flattened vivid-red bill. It can be seen along bright, sandy shores, wading on pinkish

Willet

legs. The black oystercatcher lives on the Pacific coast. It is somewhat smaller and lacks the white relief.

In the springtime you will see a 10-to-11-inch red-breasted bird with a short bill decorating the sandy shores of our East Coast. This handsome bird is the knot, a member of the sandpiper family. During the rest of the year it is plain and gray, with no outstanding characteristics.

The willet ranges between 14 and 17 inches in length. Its gray body, tipped with a long blue bill and blue legs, displays striking black-and-white wings in flight.

Where the breakers crash against the shore the sanderling can be seen, dashing about the beach or probing the sand in search of small invertebrates. This is a very common bird, plump and quite white, with a heavy black bill, black legs, and a conspicuous white stripe on each ring.

The most abundant birds of the California beaches are the western sandpipers, while semipalmated sandpipers dominate the New Jersey flats. Both are dark-legged, brown-gray birds, the Western variety distinguished by rusty markings, a slightly larger size, and a longer bill.

You may see the ringed plover running along the shore or flying low over the water with its wings fully extended and beating softly and slowly. This bird is 6 to 8 inches in size, with a short tail and bill, brown back, and a white breast set off by a black collar.

One member of the plover family seeks food by turning over shells and stones, hence the name of ruddy turnstone. In flight this chunky 8-to-10-inch-long bird will surely catch your eye, with its harlequin markings in black, white, and rusty red. Other characteristics are orange legs and a somewhat upturned bill, short, stout, and pointed.

The chunky, 10-inch-long surfbird is another aptly named member of the plover family, for it lives at the surf line along the Pacific coast. Its dark-gray wings have a prominent white stripe; its tail is banded with black. Black streaks the head and neck, and brown-black spots mark the breast and belly. The surfbird's upper tail and lower rump are white, and its short legs are yellow.

The common tern has a black cap, forked tail, and an orange bill tipped with black. It measures 13 to 16 inches in length. The lighter Forster's tern, found chiefly in the West, can be seen in the marshes rather than on sand beaches.

Gulls are, for many of us, a symbol of the shore. On the West Coast look for the herring gull, 22 to 26 inches long, pink-legged, and tipped with black on the wings. The western gull of the Pacific coast has yellow legs and a yellow bill with a red spot on it.

Back to Dry Land

Now it is time to put away your boots and binoculars, your hand lens and pail, and whatever other equipment you have brought along. Carry back to dry land a pocketful of prettily patterned shells, a rough but handsome starfish, and a bouquet of briny seaweed. They will help you to recall, when you are far from the surf, that exciting, changing frontier where land and sea forever embrace and separate, separate and embrace.

Forster's tern

Mount Rainier National Park, Washington

Chapter 3

ON THE MOUNTAIN

ALTHOUGH mountains are often called the eternal peaks, they are not eternal at all. They are born and grow, they crumble and die, in a process that involves great periods of geologic time.

Mountains may be folded or faulted, cone-shaped or dome-shaped. Folded mountains occur when part of the earth's surface is pushed together, causing the compressed land to wrinkle and buckle. In faulted mountains, underground pressures force a great mass of rock to break along a fault (a line of weakness) in the earth's crust, elevating the rocks on one side of the break. Mountains are also created when volcanic material is spewed upward from the bowels of the earth. Volcanic cone mountains are built of layers of lava and ash deposited on the earth's surface in great quantities. Volcanic dome mountains appear when the molten material cannot find an exit but instead forms a blister just under the overlying layer of rock.

Combinations of these mountain-building processes are responsible for the creation of the principal ranges of contiguous United States—the Appalachians, the Rockies, and the long stretch that includes the Sierra Nevadas and the Cascades.

In the West the Cascade Range begins at Lassen

Peak in California and heads north for over 700 miles to the Fraser River in British Columbia. It parallels the Pacific Coast, about 100 to 150 miles inland, and is distinguished by majestic Mount Rainier, the great cascades of the Columbia River (for which it was named), and awesome Crater Lake, rimmed with multicolored cliffs.

At Lassen Peak the Cascade Range is met by the Sierra Nevadas, which travel southeast for 400 miles to the Tehachapi Pass. The Sierra Nevadas once boasted the highest point in the United States, the 14,495-foot Mount Whitney. But when Alaska achieved statehood its Mount McKinley, 20,270 feet high, became our nation's record peak.

The great barrier between East and West is the Rocky Mountain chain, often said to comprise fifty Switzerlands. The hissing geysers of Yellowstone National Park, the plunging trench known as the Grand Canyon, the looming summit that inspired the slogan "Pikes Peak or Bust,"—all can be found in this complex 7000-to-14,000-foot-high range that sweeps from central New Mexico to Montana's Canadian border.

Along the Atlantic rise the many parallel ridges of the ancient Appalachians, lying between the St. Lawrence in Quebec and the Gulf Coastal Plain in Central Alabama—a distance of more than 1600 miles. Although there are many beauties here—the Shenandoah Valley, the Great Smoky Mountains—the Appalachians are less impressive for their scenery than for their age. The worn, low, rounded peaks, averaging only 3000 feet in height, are a testimony to erosive forces that have been at their work for millions upon millions of years, remorselessly carrying the mountains, bit by bit, down to the waiting sea.

Life Zones

Virtually every climate from balmy to polar can be experienced in the course of a journey from the base of a mountain to its summit. Because the high, dry air holds less of the warming infrared rays of the sun than moist air does, it generally gets colder and colder as you climb. On the average, temperatures drop three to five degrees every time you scale another thousand feet.

Temperatures fall, but wind velocities rise as the summit is approached. Altitude is in itself a cause of increased velocity. But winds may also travel faster when forced through narrow channels, such as those formed by two adjoining peaks. On the summit of the Appalachians' Mount Washington, the average velocity over a 24-hour period has reached 129 miles per hour. This same summit is the scene of the world's highest recorded wind velocity—231 miles per hour.

Clouds are often seen high on the mountains, settling on the crests in towering white mounds of every possible shape. These are the product of moisture-laden air, which rises from the lowlands and condenses in the chiller upper reaches. From these clouds come rainstorms, and snowstorms that may be the source of destructive avalanches.

Variations in mountain climate have resulted in distinctly different types of plant and animal life, arranged in interlacing horizontal bands—called life zones—from bottom to top. Equivalent life zones may vary from mountain to mountain and from east slope to west slope. But on all ranges you will see a fairly steady progression from the relatively easy living of the lower regions to the dramatic hardships of the mountain top.

Almost every range has forested slopes. In the Sierra Nevadas, flatlands and foothills give way to a belt of western pine, called the Transition Zone, where summers are warm and dry and some snow falls in the cool winter. Beginning anywhere from 5500 to 8000 feet (depending on the location of the slope) is the Canadian Zone, a belt of lodgepole pine and red fir, with cool summers and heavy, persistent snow in the cold winter. Somewhere above 7000 or 8000 feet is the Hudsonian Zone, also known as the subalpine belt. Here the forests are sparse, and killing frosts may occur in any month.

As you move higher still, the trees become smaller and lower, in some places growing horizontally. On most mountains you come, finally, to the timberline, an uneven boundary between the last trees and the treeless slopes beyond.

Continue now up into the tundra land, a place of rolling high-mountain meadows and naked rocks known as the Arctic-Alpine Zone. Even in this desolate region a hardy vegetation flourishes—mosses, lichens, sedges, and miniature flowering plants. On some mountains these growing things climb to the very top, or are halted only at the domains of perpetual ice and snow.

Alpine Plants

In the Arctic-Alpine Zone, the region where no trees grow, the showy flowering plants provide, for a brief season, carpets of glowing color. Small, low-lying, slow to develop, these plants are discouraged in innumerable ways from clinging to their precarious perch, but they cling there nevertheless.

Nature confronts tundra plants with raging winds and bitter cold, with winters that are eight months long. In addition, there are shocking shifts in soil temperature, which may drop from the warmth of a summer day to below freezing at night. Other difficulties of high-mountain life are long periods of dryness, interrupted by floods of rain, and the insecure anchorage of the shifting soil.

Plants cope by remaining dormant during the cold season and growing only during the brief summer. They develop root systems large enough to locate water and to maintain a stable place on the slope. Some have fuzz-covered leaves that serve as a windshield and heat trap, or thick, waxy coverings that resist evaporation. The typical ground-hugging nature of tundra plants is an obvious adaptation to the forceful gusts that whip the upper slopes.

Most mountain plants are perennials, for the growing season is too short to allow a plant to sprout, grow, flower, and produce seeds within a single year. The cushion pink (also called moss campion) puts most of its energy into developing large roots and may not come into full bloom for twenty years. Then it sends up many hundreds of tiny pink blossoms, set off by narrow leaves, growing in a dense cushion-shaped clump only a foot across. This circumpolar flower, found in the Scottish highlands and on the peaks of the Alps, can be seen in this country on the high, exposed ridges of the Rocky Mountains.

Another tundra member of the pink family is the sandwort, represented on Mount Washington by the mountain daisy. This is a tiny, dainty plant, growing in a dense tuft from the root, with crowded, thread-like leaves and flowers whose translucent white petals are notched at the tips.

A species of stonecrop is found on the rocky slopes of the High Sierras. This matlike, succulent plant has thick leaves arranged in basal rosettes, and clusters of yellow or white flowers joined into a tube at the base.

Under overhanging rocks and cliffs the Sierra primrose settles. It is a creeping plant with long, narrow, wedge-shaped leaves toothed at the tip. The tubular flowers, red-purple with yellow throats, display five notched lobes.

In the Rockies blooms the parry or alpine primrose, large and blood-red, with funnel-form flowers and smooth green leaves growing in a basal rosette. Surprisingly this plant stands tall and upright in a region noted for its "belly plants."

Look for the compact, leafy cushion formed by draba, a yellow-flowered plant with ovate, twisted pods. This mustard-family representative of the High Sierras has long, thick, densely clustered leaves and stems up to 3¼ inches long. Related species of draba grow in the Rockies.

On the summits of the Appalachians' White Mountains, lapland rosebay, dwarf member of the heath family, hugs the rocks. Its small leaves are olive-green and evergreen, growing in clusters on an otherwise bare stem. The five-lobed flowers are light purple and dotted.

Mats of mountain heath, with bright-pink urn-shaped flowers, grow above the timberline of the Rockies. And two types of heather, red-mountain and white, display their bell-shaped flowers in the High Sierras.

Perfect miniatures of many familiar lowland plants flourish throughout the high mountains. Look for the purply blooms of dwarf violets growing from stems under 2 inches long; for cushions of alpine forget-me-nots, composed of massed blue (or, occasionally, white) flowers, and leaves and stems covered with long, soft, white hairs; for the enormous yellow heads and narrow, woolly leaves of alpine sunflowers.

A widely distributed tundra plant is the dryad, also known as alpine avens. This is the largest, white-flowered, mat-forming plant of the Rockies' alpine zone, displaying toothed leathery leaves that can roll up and woody stems topped with solitary flowers.

On mountain summits in the northern Appalachians grows the alpine goldenrod, a dwarf species about 8 inches high. The flowers, which have about twelve rays, cluster thickly at the top of a stout stem.

Species of a flat-topped plant called yarrow bloom in the Western mountains, exhibiting white or yellow flower clusters. The small flowers are of two types—elongated rays and short disks.

Other tundra plants include nodding bellflowers, brilliant gentians, clover, and members of the figwort and saxifrage families. Elephanthead is a figwort whose dense spike of small, reddish-purple-to-pink flowers distinctly resembles an elephant's head with an upcurved trunk. Purple saxifrage bears a small wine-colored flower with clusters of fleshy leaves growing in dense tufts.

Snowbanks provide a shelter for many alpine plants because temperatures beneath 2½ feet of snow never drop below 27 degrees, no matter how cold the air temperature becomes. The dainty snow buttercup grows comfortably 12 feet under a drift, producing an elaborate system of roots and tiny, shiny, bright-yellow blooms. During its short stay in the open air the leaves of this buttercup manufacture enough food to survive for one or even more frozen winters.

Another plant found in the snow-accumulation areas of the Rockies is the glacier lily, whose nodding yellow head (or heads) bobs from a naked stem rising from two large and shiny basal leaves. Glacier lilies seem to climb the mountain as the weather warms, golden fields of them appearing beside a stretch of still-unmelted snow.

Sky pilot grows on the Rockies' highest peaks, putting out purple, broadly funnel-shaped flowers and thirty to forty whorled leaflets, round and rather sticky. When stepped on, this plant gives off a powerful skunk odor.

Glacier lilies

Wapiti, the American elk

High-Mountain Mammals

Mountain mammals properly include many creatures you will meet in the forests, deserts, and plains of North America, for the lower life zones harbor all these forms of life. Here, however, we will concentrate on some of the mammals of the upper mountains, mammals that have managed by hibernation, winter migration, or other adaptations to deal with the bitter cold of the high altitudes.

The American elk and the bighorn sheep were once dwellers of the lowlands until driven away by hunters and farmers. The Rocky Mountain goat, on the other hand, always lived in the upper regions. But all three of these herbivores–immigrants and native–handle the slopes with a skill and grace that climbers and skiers might well envy.

Wapiti is the Indian name for the American elk which is, with the exception of the moose, the largest deer in the world. Full grown, a wapiti stands 5 feet 4 inches tall at the shoulder and weighs from 700 to 1000 pounds. Its head sports tremendous antlers, sharp and many-pronged, which may measure 60 inches from tip to tip.

The wapiti is a pale fawn shade, relieved by dark chestnut-brown on the head and mane and by straw coloring on the rump patch and short tail. In the summer months it browses on the heights of the Rockies and the mountains of the Far West. In the cold months it avoids the deep winter snows by migrating below the timberline to sheltered valleys.

The bighorn sheep of the Rockies and Far West frequently follows the seasons, leaving the treeless zone when the weather cools. You may see them jumping from ledge to precipitous ledge, taking 20-foot leaps at breakneck speeds and landing effortlessly on hard, slippery surfaces, thanks to the slip-proof, shock-absorbent pads of their hoofs. The bighorn male is easily identified by its great curled horns, often curved into a full circle.

In summer the bighorn (also known as the mountain sheep) is dark- or gray-brown; its coat turns lighter and grayer in wintertime. Instead of the typical woolly fur of the sheep family, the bighorn wears a covering of long, coarse, stiff hairs. A large patch of whitish hairs appears on the rump. This substantial-looking beast measures about 40 inches at the shoulder and weighs between 175 and 350 pounds. Its sensory organs are very well developed—sharp eyesight, excellent hearing, and an exceptionally acute sense of smell.

Although it very much resembles a true goat, the Rocky Mountain goat is more closely related to the chamois of Europe and is categorized as a goat antelope. Able to make do with the sparsest winter forage, and protected by its thick shaggy coat from the cruelest winter blasts, it can live above the timberline all year round while its less hardy companions head for the lower slopes.

The handsome Rocky Mountain goat is white all over, the color set off by two slender, daggerlike black horns that measure 10 inches in length. The black hoofs are perfectly designed for mountain travel, with razor-sharp rims that grip and soft heel pads that cling. Full-grown males stand between 35 and 40 inches at the shoulder and weigh between 150 and 300 pounds. Both sexes are bearded.

A Rocky Mountain goat can scale almost perpendicular cliffs, pulling itself up by its powerful forelegs. It has also been observed glissading purposively, all four feet together, down a 70-degree snow-covered slope.

Second largest of the New World cats (the jaguar holds the record) is the fierce, flesh-eating cougar, known also as mountain lion, puma, panther, painter, and catamount. A well-distributed predator, it is found in all our western mountains, ranging up to the brushy, forested country of the Sierras' Canadian Zone. As you climb the higher slopes you may be literally stopped in your tracks by the wild, hair-raising shriek of this cat of the mountains.

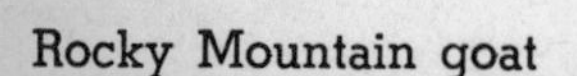
Rocky Mountain goat

Cougar

The cougar is a lithe, tawny, short-haired creature with a feline face and a powerful 4-foot body terminating in a slender 2½-foot tail. It weighs about 160 pounds but moves with soundless grace in pursuit of deer and elk. Capable of springing 20 feet in one leap, the cougar has also been known to jump safely from a perch located 60 feet from the ground.

The grizzly bear or silvertip, a carnivore that is perfectly content with a meal of berries, grass, or other vegetation, once dominated the American Northwest. Only a few hundred exist today, however, and their broad distribution has shrunk to the confines of our National Parks. The Canadian Zone of the Rocky Mountains harbors some of these great beasts.

The grizzly has a thick, dark-brown fur coat, heavily tipped with white on the back, which presents the "grizzled" appearance for which the bear is named. Its massive 6-to-8-foot-long body, averaging about 500 pounds, has a short tail and a distinct hump over the shoulders. The broad head is topped with brief ears, and long, curved claws appear at the end of paws powerful enough to break the neck of an ox or the back of an elk with one blow.

Grizzly bear

The grizzly walks with a shuffling gait, traveling great distances in search of food and even crossing snow-capped mountain peaks. In the winter it returns to a den for a long sleep. Unlike true hibernators, however, the grizzly's temperature does not drop far below normal and it may emerge for a brief period on a mild midwinter day.

Rodents are the most common mammals of the mountains. Two that can't be overlooked are the bushy-tailed wood rat, found chiefly in the Rockies as high as 13,000 feet, and the yellow-bellied marmot, which often ranges beyond the timberline.

The bushy-tailed wood rat is a most attractive member of the pack-rat group, those collectors of coins, nails, glass, rags, and any other little items they can lay their paws on—including false teeth! With its soft, sandy-brown fur, shiny black eyes, and a bushy tail almost as long as the rest of itself, this rat has a distinctly squirrel-like appearance. A large one may weigh over a pound and measure 17 inches from nose tip to tail tip.

The yellow-bellied marmot is a high-mountain relative of the woodchuck or groundhog. Its stout body, colored a grizzled yellow-brown on top and buff below, is borne on short legs and feet. The blackish face is marked with a narrow white band. From nose to rump this 7-pound member of the ground-squirrel tribe measures 14 to 18 inches; beyond is another 5 to 8 inches of tail.

While the bushy-tailed wood rat is active all year round, the yellow-bellied marmot hibernates in winter. When spring returns it comes out of its den beneath a rock pile, skinny but intact.

The pika, or rock rabbit, or cony (not to be confused with the subungulate conies, mentioned on page 146), is a relative of the true rabbit. It industriously prepares for the winter months by cutting grasses and weeds and spreading them out to dry among the rocks. During the cold season these little piles of hay, stored in a snug den, provide a satisfactory food supply, essential for high-mountain creatures that neither hibernate nor migrate to the sheltered valleys below.

The 6-to-7-inch pika has a red-tinged pale-gray color that blends with the lichen and mosses growing on the mountain rocks. It looks like a miniature rabbit, except for its short ears, lack of external tail, and

Bushy-tailed wood rat

abbreviated forelegs. This sturdy cliff-dweller, found in the West as far as the Rockies, basks in the warm sunshine but can vanish from its rocky perch in a twinkling of an eye if disturbed. Listen for its unusual voice, which is sometimes a sharp whistle, sometimes a lamblike bleat.

Snowshoe rabbit, or varying hare

The snowshoe rabbit may be found at high elevations in the northern mountains, where it dines on grasses, herbs, and twigs. Its name appropriately describes its oversized feet (in winter only), which provide substantial support on the soft snow. Equally appropriate is its other name, the varying hare—a reference to the change of its coat color from red-brown in summer to white in wintertime. Adults weigh about 5 pounds, with the 13-to-18-inch head and body terminating in a 1½-to-2-inch tail.

High-Mountain Reptiles

Various reptiles have been recorded high on the mountain slopes. Look for the southern mountain lizard, found at 9000 feet in southern California, and the common western skink, up to 8000 feet.

For a few months each year the western fence lizard makes its home in the High Sierras. This reptile may total 8¾ inches in length, more than half of which is tail. The upper body is blackish, deep brown, or gray, with dark spots arranged in lengthwise rows; the lower body is whitish with dark markings. Touches of yellow or orange brighten the thighs, and a blue coloring appears on the throat and belly in the male.

The northern alligator lizard ascends to the Sierra's subalpine belt, pursuing its activities both by day and dusk, wriggling along the ground, climbing trees, and sometimes even swimming. Its body is dark-marked brown or olive above, gray to yellow below. Its long tail may be double the length of its 3½-to-6-inch head and body.

Representatives of the smooth green snake appear in the mountains of East and West. This is a gentle reptile, bright green in color above, and white or yellow-white below. Lengths range, on the average, between 14 and 20 inches.

The black rat snake, also called the mountain black snake, climbs to high altitudes in parts of the Appalachians. Shiny and black with occasional traces of a spotted pattern, this snake displays areas of white, yellow, orange, or red on the skin between the scales. Chin and throat are light, and the light-colored belly has shadings of gray or brown. Average lengths are 42 to 72 inches, but a 101-incher has officially been recorded.

At 1000 to 2000 feet, and sometimes even higher, the Appalachian crowned snake can be found. It has a black cap on the head, a brown body with fifteen rows of smooth scales, and a white belly sometimes tinged with pink or yellow. This reptile is small and secretive.

Common in the mountainous regions of the Northeast, the timber rattlesnake has two major color patterns. You may see timber rattlers that are yellow, brown, or gray, with dark V-shaped crossbands. Or a heavy stippling of black or deep brown may almost obliterate the lighter body coloring, resulting sometimes in completely black specimens.

The western diamondback rattlesnake will ascend 5000 feet or more into the mountains. This brown or gray reptile is marked with a diamond pattern and measures from 30 to 72 inches. Like other rattlesnakes, it has a loud, buzzing rattle and will fearlessly maintain its position when encountered.

In the Sierras western rattlesnakes have climbed 9000 or 10,000 feet, with one record breaker reaching the 11,000 mark. Broad-headed, heavy-bodied, this snake is yellow- or gray-brown, with dark blotches along the back and two rows of small dark spots on the sides.

In Colorado the wandering garter snake has wandered above 10,000 feet. Garter snakes are also found at high elevations in the Sierras from late May into October.

High-Mountain Insects

Like other forms of life, insects appear wherever they can survive, even high on the mountains.

The up-to-1-inch grylloblatta, relative of grasshoppers and crickets, is a slim, wingless creature with short legs. It thrives deep in crevices under the snow, above 7000 feet in the Sierras and up as high as 12,000 feet.

Species of dragonflies and damselflies are found at high elevations in all our mountains. These are among the most beautiful of insects, with two pairs of long, narrow wings that are net-veined, transparent, and sometimes colorfully patterned. The body is elongated, the eyes almost cover the surface of the head, and the antennae are very short. Distinguish between dragonflies and damselflies in these ways: dragons are stronger fliers and larger-bodied; at rest dragons hold their wings outstretched while damsels hold them together over the back.

In the Arctic-Alpine Zone of some New England mountains (Mount Washington, New Hampshire, and Mount Katahdin, Maine), butterflies of the genus *Oeneis* will be seen. These are drab-colored, extremely hairy insects, capable of enduring bitterly cold climates. Representatives of a group called the Lesser Fritillaries also appear in the arctic regions of the eastern mountains. These butterflies are small and orange-brown with black markings. Many Sierra butterflies reach the subalpine belt and some of them

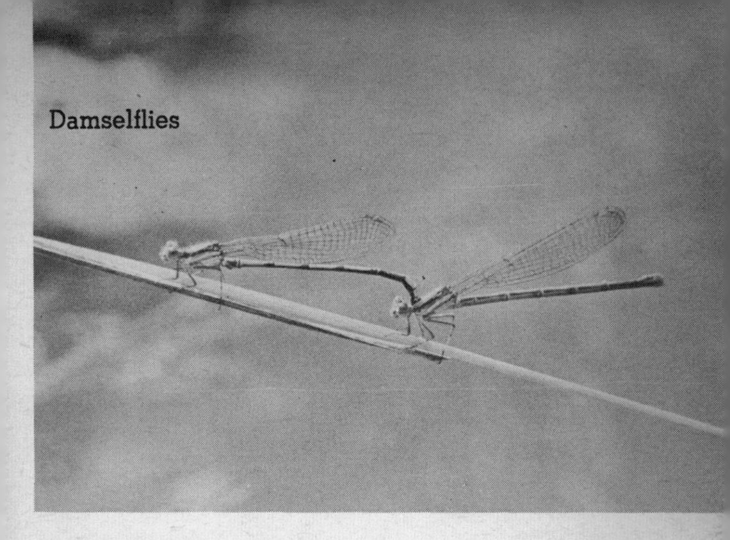
Damselflies

keep right on going into the Arctic-Alpine Zone. Among them are the Nevada dusky wing, a dark-brown insect with small, pale-colored spots on the forewings, and the ivallda arctic, a western species of *Oeneis*, with ashy coloring and a few small spots.

The ground beetle, blackish and long-legged, is common at all elevations in the Sierras, including the higher mountain regions. So is the predaceous diving beetle, an oval, smooth, shiny insect.

All our high-mountain regions harbor crane flies, noted for long fragile legs that break off very easily. A wingless, spiderlike representative appears in the High Sierras.

Other insects of the upper altitudes include spider wasps, yellow jackets, and bumblebees. In the Sierras the wasp occurs in all but the topmost regions, and the black-and-yellow yellow jacket rises to 8000 feet. Bumblebees buzz on the alpine slopes, pollinating many flowering plants.

Birds of the High Mountains

Many birds make permanent or part-time homes in the upper life zones of the mountains. Look beside high rushing streams for the chunky, slate-colored water ouzel, also known as the dipper, whose clear, ringing song can be heard throughout the year. This Westerner is shaped like a large wren, with a short tail, pale legs, and white eyelids.

The only ptarmigan in western United States is the white-tailed resident of the mountains' alpine summits. In summer this is a brown bird with white on its belly, wings, and tail. In winter the ptarmigan is white all over, except for black eyes and a black bill.

Ptarmigan

Gliding and soaring through the mountain sky, the imposing golden eagle displays great wings with a 7-foot spread. Its plumage is a deep brown, relieved by a gold-brown head, and its size exceeds that of all other bird residents of the Sierras.

An avian family called the Fringillidae, distinguished by its short, stout bill, has some important western-mountain representatives. The male Cassin's finch has a crimson crown, a pale-pink rump and breast, and dusky streaks and red tinges on his dark-brown back, wings, and tail. The male pine grosbeak is a dull rose-red, with two white bars on his dark wings. A light-gray patch marks the head of the gray-crowned rosy finch, a dark-brown bird washed with pink on rump and wings. Black-and-white stripes mark the head of the white-crowned sparrow, an attractive gray-breasted bird.

Listen for the mellow, tinkling song of Audubon's warbler, which ranges up to the Sierra's subalpine belt. In the springtime the male is blue-gray above, with a heavy splotch of black at the breast, and yellow on throat, crown, rump, and side patches.

Golden eagle

Clark's nutcracker dwells high in the Sierras above 9000 feet. This is a light-gray bird, built like a crow, with outstanding white patches on its black wings and black central feathers on its white tail.

A white stripe over each eye distinguishes the mountain chickadee, a gray-bodied bird with black on the chin, throat, and head. These busy, acrobatic little birds hunt for insect food among the twigs and foliage of trees, often hanging upside down as they search.

The male mountain bluebird is a good-looking Westerner with a lovely turquoise body. Like so many male birds, he far outshines the female of the species, who in this case is a dull brown with a few touches of blue.

West and East share some of the same mountain birds. Those common to both regions include the red crossbill, the pine siskin, and the hermit thrush. The male crossbill is brick-red with dark wings and tail and a crossed bill. The pine siskin is small, dark, and heavily streaked, with a touch of yellow on the wings and on the deeply notched tail. The hermit thrush is brown with a spotted breast and a reddish tail.

Mountain bluebird

In the East, where the mountains are not very high, there are not many high-mountain birds. Two to look for, however, are the gray-cheeked thrush and the blackpoll warbler. The thrush, olive- or gray-brown, is named for its grayish cheeks. The male warbler is a striped gray bird in spring, with white cheeks and a black cap on his head.

Down in the Valley

As you travel downward from the high peaks you will pass through ever gentler climates until you reach the mild lowlands. The plants you left behind were brief-blooming, the animals elusive, the winds bitter, and the temperatures low. But the sights of the alpine slopes are well worth climbing a mountain to see.

Bison

Chapter 4

ON THE GREAT PLAINS

LOOK westward beyond the Mississippi River and you will see a tawny sea of waving grass under a cloudless sky. This vast, treeless country, level or slightly rolling, is the Great Plains of the United States.

Between Canada on the north and the Mexican border on the south, the plains extend for more than 1600 miles. The Rockies define their western limits, but on the east the boundary is less clear. Some say the Great Plains end, roughly, where corn, cotton, or other intensively grown crops become dominant over wheat. Some simply call the Mississippi River the eastern boundary. Some place the border at the 98th meridian, giving the plains a span of about 750 miles at the widest point. Using this line of demarcation, we can say that the Great Plains occupy a fifth of the nation (586,461 square miles of land) and include portions of Montana, Wyoming, Colorado, New Mexico, the Dakotas, Nebraska, Kansas, Oklahoma, and Texas.

The Climate of the Great Plains

The plains are neither humid, subhumid, nor arid. They are, rather, a semiarid land with dry, parched years punctuated by choking duststorms, and years of violent rainstorms, heavy hail, and flood. Throughout most of the area the average annual rainfall is under 20 inches, decreasing from east to west. The amount that actually falls in a given year, however, is quite variable, for precipitation depends on the accidental collision of two of the three great air masses that sweep unimpeded and unpredictably across the plains—down from Canada and the Hudson Bay, up from the Gulf of Mexico, and over the Rockies from the Pacific Ocean.

Evaporation on the Great Plains is high, thus cutting down the effectiveness of the rainfall. Evaporation is hastened by the bright sunshine and the high winds.

These winds that whip the plains—hot and dry in the summer, biting cold in the winter—are harder and steadier than those in any other part of the country, except at certain seashores. The chinook is a warm wind blowing down from the mountain into a colder region, the "norther" a cold wind from the north descending into a warm area and producing a speedy temperature drop of 25 to 50 degrees. The blizzard, a word used loosely in the East to describe a severe snowstorm, is actually a name that was specifically invented for the winter terror of the plains, "a mad, rushing combination of wind and snow which neither man nor beast could face." Summertime brings another terror—high winds in the form of tornadoes. These black funnel-shaped clouds twist across the land, ravishing buildings and crops for miles and miles.

The span between high and low temperatures on the Great Plains is exceptional. In the summer the thermometer may pass 100 degrees F. In the cruelly cold winter temperatures may drop far below zero. Dramatic temperature variations occur not only seasonally but even within the same day, transforming a cool morning into a burning afternoon, or following a blizzard with a warm, snow-melting wind.

Efforts to find a pattern in the major climate changes of the plains have so far proven unsuccessful. Studies of the past offer no basis for future prediction except this rueful rule of thumb: Expect anything, and be prepared for the worst.

The Grasslands

When you walk upon the plains, forget about trees and flowers and all other members of the plant kingdom except one—grass. There are occasional trees, of course, and bright-blooming wildflowers do lend a touch of color to the scene. But the Great Plains are, above all, a grassland, covered with both the natural vegetation that first swept the area in ancient times and the cultivated, man-grown crops (wheat, barley, corn, oats, rye, and sorghum) that supply you with your breakfast cereals, your corn on the cob, and your daily bread.

North America's native grasslands actually extend beyond what is technically called the Great Plains to meet the forests on the east. The region between plains and forest is called the true prairie, a place of fairly humid climate where the grasses are tall and luxuriant, the soil dark, deep, and fertile. Gradually merging into the semiarid grasslands of the Great Plains, prairie becomes steppe—a region of short grasses.

Conspicuous among the tall grasses of the American prairie is the robust big bluestem, with leafy flower stalks 4 to 7 feet high. Big bluestem has forked flower clusters, called racemes, which are mostly purplish in color. Strong underground runners, called rhizomes, extend from the base, putting out shoots and roots. This erect perennial furnishes good yields of hay as well as a nutritious and highly favored forage for cattle.

While the big bluestem is characteristic of lowland prairies, its close relative, little bluestem, with flower stalks of 1 to 3 feet, may be found in the up-

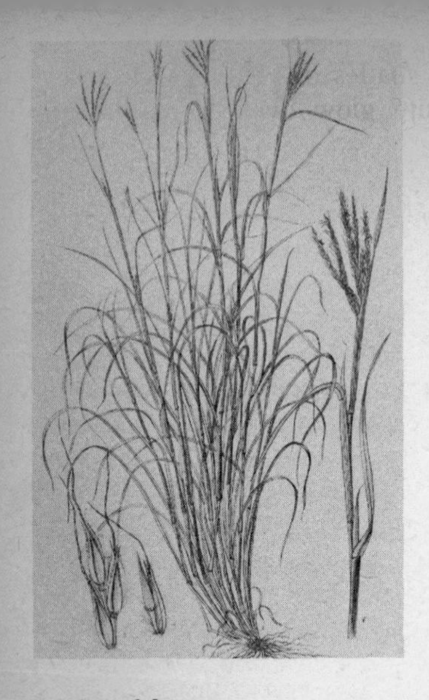

Big bluestem

Little bluestem

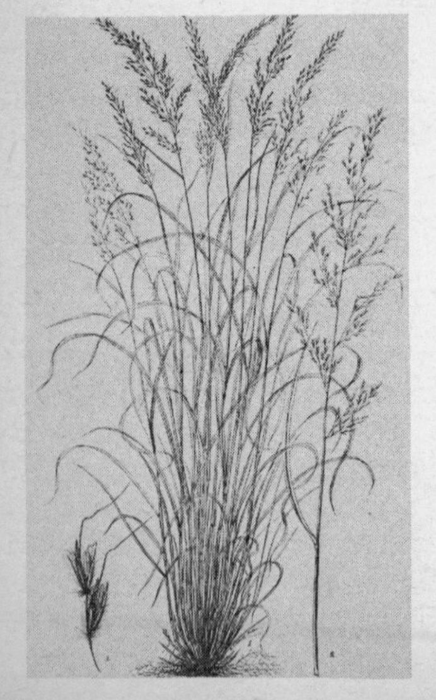

Indian grass

lands. This grass dries to shades of yellow, red, and bronze, casting an exquisite glow over the autumn and winter landscape.

The tall, warm-season Indian grass resembles big bluestem except for its flowers. Indian grass has large flower clusters, called panicles, which are golden in color.

Needlegrass is, typically, an upland perennial, with flower stalks 2 to 4 feet tall. Its leaves, smooth and shiny below, corrugated and waxy above, roll inward during drought and are green throughout the winter months. You will find needlegrass growing in small circular bunches, widely spaced and intermixed with other grasses.

Standing 4 to 7 feet tall, switchgrass sends down roots 6 to 10 feet into the ground. This is a beautiful grass, pale-green in color, heavily tufted, slim-bladed, and decorated with a topping of delicate flower heads. The shallowly rooted, slender wheat grass, a drought-resistant, cool-season perennial, is still another important member of the tall-grass community.

As you move westward you enter the region of short grasses. There you will find the hardy buffalo grass, various grama grasses, western wheat grass, and galleta.

Buffalo grass is a warm-season perennial that becomes green late in spring and dries early in fall. Only a few inches tall, it has spikelike flower clusters and narrow 1-to-4-inch leaves that are hairy and curled. Buffalo grass puts out slender surface runners, sometimes 2 or 2½ feet long, which form a thick continuous sod so tough that pioneers used it to build houses and fences. The runners of the buffalo grass distinguish it from the blue grama, which otherwise has a very similar appearance. Like buffalo grass, it forms a low, continuous covering over large areas of the plains, and provides good pasture for cattle.

Another member of the big grama clan is the hairy grama, named for its very hairy leaves. It sprawls low on the ground and sends up slender flower stems from a large but sparsely leafed base.

Switchgrass

Hairy grama

Side oats grama is the most widespread of the grama grasses. Taller (sometimes over 2 feet) and more luxuriant than blue grama, it looks like a rounded whisk broom. The leaves are somewhat hairy and the slender flower stalks bear pendulous spikes.

Look for the distinctive blue-green foliage and flower stalks of western wheat grass. Its stiff, abundant leaves are long and narrow, ridged and rough on the upper surface but smooth below, and capable of rolling inward during drought. Flower stalks stand up to 4 feet high, terminating in prominent spikes. Long, branched rhizomes permit this wheat grass to spread far and wide.

The erect, highly drought-resistant galleta is a perennial with flower stalks up to 20 inches long. Its large, tough, woody, soil-binding rhizomes extend from the base but do not form a continuous sod. Instead, this grass grows in bunches or large mats, sending up narrow and rather short leaves that are rigid, blue, and hairy.

Galleta

Like desert plants, the native grasses of the plains have adapted to a climate characterized by long periods of drought. Many have drought-resistant traits which reduce exposure to the sun and decrease evaporation, such as hairy leaves, leaves that roll up, oily or waxy coatings, a grayer coloring, a thicker skin. Some grasses conserve moisture by sending their roots deep into the soil. Others are able to hasten or postpone maturity, grow tall or remain short, depending on conditions. Dormancy during drought is still another way of coping with the difficulties of climate on the plains.

Mammals of the Plains

The grasslands of the Great Plains support a thriving animal life, both imported and domestic. The cattle of the range, which seem so characteristic, were actually brought in from other countries. But there is a distinctive native population too, including buffaloes and American antelopes, jackrabbits and prairie dogs, badgers, coyotes, and wolves.

A hundred years ago some 50 or 60 million buffaloes moved slowly and clumsily across the open land. Today the great herds are gone, shot down by the hunter's gun. Numbered in the thousands now, these imposing beasts live under strict protection to insure their survival. No walk on the Great Plains would be complete without a look at the mammal which was once its undisputed king.

The buffalo is really a bison, for unlike the true buffaloes of Asia and Africa it has a hump over its shoulders. The massive head sprouts short, stout, curved horns; a long black beard hangs from the chin of the male; and the small tail is generously tasseled. A male buffalo may measure over 10 feet and sometimes weighs more than a ton.

Buffaloes have heavy winter coats, dark-brown and shaggy, which are seasonally shed. This shedding is only one of the many adjustments that admirably suit them for life on the Great Plains. They are also able to endure great extremes of heat and cold. When caught in one of the blizzards that periodically rage over the plains, buffaloes face into the storm instead of drifting with it, as cattle do. Thus they avoid being swept off ledges or embankments to their death.

The American or pronghorn antelope, which is not a true antelope, is certainly a true resident of the Great Plains, its exclusive home. Unlike any other ungulate, it sports branched, hollow horns which are shed annually. (The female's horns are smaller and sometimes she has none at all.)

The pronghorn weighs 100 to 125 pounds and

Pronghorn antelope

Black-tailed prairie dogs

wears a coat of rich red-brown or tan with a black-brown mane. A white patch on the rump, composed of long hairs, stands erect in a great rosette when the animal is alarmed, brilliantly reflecting the light and thus warning other herd members of danger. From a gland in this rump patch a musky odor is thrown off as an additional signal. Even more impressive than these warnings, however, is the pronghorn's response to them. It can flee at 60 miles an hour, a speed faster than that of any other animal on this continent.

Just as a buffalo isn't a buffalo and a pronghorn antelope isn't an antelope, a jackrabbit isn't a rabbit but a hare. Short forelegs and long, highly developed hind legs make these burro-eared creatures among the fleetest on the plains. The white-tailed jackrabbits achieve speeds of 45 miles an hour and leaps of up to 18 to 20 feet. "All they ask of a coyote," it has been said, "is a fair start and an open field."

As you walk on the Great Plains you may come

across the home of the prairie dog, which is not a dog, of course, but a species of ground squirrel. Prairie-dog towns are complex interconnected burrows several feet underground, capable of housing hundreds, thousands, perhaps even millions of inhabitants within a maze of intersecting tunnels. Sharp-eyed guards patrol the entrance holes, which are distinctively ringed with firm, high mounds of earth to prevent flooding. When danger appears, the guards bark a warning.

There are two main kinds of prairie dogs, the black-tailed and the smaller white-tailed. Be on the lookout for these sharp-toothed, 14-inch-long creatures, with warm-weather fur that is red-brown on top and yellow-white below, and winter fur of pale buff.

Unlike the mammals mentioned so far, the badger is a carnivore as well as a vegetarian. Its general coloring is gray, with a white-marked face, and its stocky, short-legged body, weighing 12 to 24 pounds, measures about 2 feet from nose to abbreviated tail. The badger's long, powerful claws can dig into the ground with amazing speed. It tunnels 4 or 5 feet below the surface, carves out a den, and lines it with dry leaves or grass.

If you are walking on the Great Plains after sundown you may hear the evening song of the coyote. This weird serenade carries for quite a distance across the land, often startling unprepared travelers with a series of yaps, barks, whines, howls, and yowls. The coyote, also known as the "prairie wolf," is one of the flesh eaters of the plains. Horace Greeley once described this unpopular scavenger as a "sneaking, cowardly little wretch." More charitable observers, emphasizing appearance over personality, point out that the coyote is really a very attractive animal. It has a handsome coat of thick long fur, gray or tawny above and white below, and a slender body weighing between 20 and 30 pounds. Its total length is about 4 feet, one third of which is a bushy, black-tipped tail.

The wolf, like the coyote, is a member of the dog

Badger

Coyote

family, a 4-foot-long creature with an additional 20 inches of tail. Some weigh as much as 175 pounds, and the record high (a wolf shot in Alaska) is 197. The common wolf is called the gray wolf but its long, thick coat may vary from black to brown to yellow to white. It, too, raises its voice after the sun goes down, sending forth a tremulous, drawn-out howl that will remain with you long after the plains are left behind.

Reptiles of the Plains

Often the grasslands are gently ruffled by a scurrying lizard or a wriggling snake. Let's take a look at a few of the reptiles that have made their home on the Great Plains.

Among the lizards is the slender glass lizard, a snaky, legless creature between 22 and 42 inches long with a dark middorsal stripe and dark stripes on the lower sides. The short-horned lizard, member of a group inaccurately called "horned toads," is brown or gray with stubby, abbreviated horns. A row of small dark spots decorate the light- to reddish-brown prairie lizard, with one bold light stripe underlining the dots and another appearing along the lower side of the body. The smooth and shiny Great Plains skink is a light tan or gray lizard, with obliquely set scales edged in black or dark brown.

The numerous snakes of the plains include species somewhat similar to those you will encounter on your desert walk: the coral, the diamondback rattler, the bullsnake, and the kingsnake. The Texas long-nosed snake, a resident of deserts and dry grasslands, is black, red, and yellow, strongly speckled, and distinguished by a pointed, protruding, or upturned snout. Whipsnakes, also found in the desert, have a plains representative in the western coachwhip, a slender, fast-moving snake usually of a uniform brownish coloring.

The western hognose snake, sometimes called the prairie rooter, is about 16 to 21 inches long with a sharply upturned snout and a slim, tapered tail at the end of its stout body. Its upper parts are brown, gray, or yellow with dark blotches; its belly is black. When frightened, the hognose flattens its head and neck, fills its body with air, and sends forth a hostile hiss.

Like most garter snakes, the plains garter is longitudinally striped, the center of its three distinct stripes an orange or orange-yellow shade. The basic color of its upper part is gray-green, olive, or brown, and it measures between 20 and 28 inches. The garter snake fights its enemies by emitting musk from a gland in its tail, sometimes following this up with vigorous striking and biting.

The 24-to-36-inch-long Great Plains rat snake has a spear-point-shaped blotch between the eyes and other blotches of gray or brown scattered upon its light gray body. Sometimes four dusky longitudinal stripes are present.

All dangerously poisonous snakes but the corals are included in the group known as the pit vipers. Both copperheads and rattlesnakes are pit vipers and both have their representatives in the grasslands.

The broad-banded copperhead is 22 to 30 inches long. Red- or chestnut-brown cross bands mark the body, and the tip of the tail is green-gray.

The western massasauga can be distinguished from other rattlers in its range by a group of nine large plates on the crown of its head. (Other pit vipers have small scales on the top of the head.) Body length averages between 18 and 26 inches, rattle not included, and the light- or tan-gray color is punctuated with dark-brown blotches.

The prairie rattler is very abundant on the Great Plains. Narrow borders of white set off the dark-brown blotches that mark its green-tinged gray, olive, or brown body. Considerably longer than the massasauga, it measures 35 to 45 inches, exclusive of rattle. There is a legend that this snake lives harmoniously with the prairie dog and the burrowing owl. Don't believe it. The rattler enjoys both of them not for their companionship but for their food value.

Grasshopper

Great Plains Insects

Grassland arthropods include spiders, various beetles, wasps and bees and ants, mosquitoes and flies, stink bugs, and chinch bugs. But the most well-known, most dramatized, most destructive, and most historic is the grasshopper.

This insect has been man's enemy since Biblical times and even today causes agricultural catastrophes that cost millions of dollars. In addition to devouring entire crops, grasshoppers feed on range grasses, sometimes reducing the supply to a point where it can no longer support cattle.

There are five common grasshopper species to look for on your walk. One is the migratory grasshopper, a 1-inch-long, reddish-brown insect with a black patch on the collar. Another is the differential grasshopper, which is ½ inch longer than the migratory. It is usually yellow, with clear, glossy outer wings and distinctive black markings. The two-striped grasshopper is named for the pair of light-colored stripes that run from head to wing tips. Its 1¼-inch body is yellow-green with dark markings and colorless wings. The fourth troublesome species is the red-legged grasshopper, about ¾ inch long, red-brown above and yellow below, with red-tinged hind legs and no-color wings. Last is the clear-winged grasshopper, a 1-inch insect with a yellow to dark-brown body. Only its underwings are clear; the outer wings have large, dark-brown blotches.

Birds of the Great Plains

Birds of the grasses and grassland ponds and marshes are plentiful. Among the water and shore birds of the Great Plains you will find the eared grebe, a small diver with a thin neck and dark back; the redhead, a gray diving duck with a black chest, a round red-brown head, and a blue black-tipped bill; the ducklike coot, distinguished from ducks by its smaller head and chicken-type bill; the avocet; the long-billed curlew; and Wilson's phalarope, trim, dark-winged, white-rumped. Many others can be seen in and around the waters, but on this walk we will concentrate on the land birds.

The prairie falcon displays blackish patches in its wingpits as it streaks over the grasslands. This streamlined bird of prey has a long tail, pointed wings which spread 3½ feet, and a pale, sandy coloring.

If you are taking your walk in the springtime be sure to catch one of the best shows on the Great Plains—the song and dance of the male prairie chicken. The song is a hollow booming sound, the dance a stomping of feet accompanied by the erection of

Long-billed curlew

black, hornlike neck feathers and the inflation of orange air sacs on the side of the neck. The prairie chicken is brown, henlike, and heavily barred, with an abbreviated dark, round tail.

The sage grouse is about the size of a small turkey, grayish in color with a black belly patch. Like the male prairie chicken, the black-throated male sage grouse is a dancer. During his performance he puffs out his white chest, exposes yellow air sacs on his neck, and raises and spreads his spiky tail feathers.

That small, brown owl you see standing on a fence post or on the ground is the burrowing owl if it has a round head, a stubby tail, and unusually long legs (for an owl). You may also encounter this burrower in its underground home—a deserted badger or gopher hole.

An exceptionally pretty bird of the grassland region is the scissor-tailed flycatcher, which gets its name from a dramatically long, scissorlike tail. Body color is a pale pearl-gray, set off by salmon-pink sides and wing linings.

Two small, black horns sit on the head of the horned lark, a brown, black-whiskered ground bird with a dark shield under a light-colored throat. You can hear this bird singing as it soars across the sky.

The western meadowlark also sings, occasionally, while on the wing, which is probably why it came to be called a lark although it is much more closely related in flight and, structure to the blackbird. This cheery flier is chunky and brown, with a conspicuous white patch on each side of its short, wide tail and a black V marking its bright yellow breast.

About the size of a house sparrow, the dickcissel looks like a miniature meadowlark with its yellow breast and black bib. The unusual name comes from its staccato dick-ciss-ciss-ciss song.

The male lark bunting in spring is slightly larger than a house sparrow, with a black body and a large, white wing patch. The lark sparrow is well marked—a black tail with white in the corners, chestnut ear patches, a striped crown, and a single spot in the center of its breast. Brewer's sparrow is small, pale and finely streaked, with a solid crown and a clear breast.

Before you leave the plains look for these three longspurs—the chestnut-collared, McCown's, and Smith's. The breeding male of the first has a black breast and belly and, not surprisingly, a chestnut collar. McCown's male breeder has a black cap and a splash of black on the breast. Smith's longspur is buff, the male deepening in color during the spring and displaying a white cheek spot clearly outlined with a triangle of black.

Out of the Plains

You may leave the semiarid grasslands by crossing the Rockies to the dry deserts of the West or by crossing the 98th meridian toward the humid timberlands of the East. You leave behind a difficult land where only the tough plants and animals survive, because food and moisture are frequently scarce and the climate is basically unreasonable. It is a land that defeated the American pioneer time and again until he learned to adapt himself, his crops, and his cattle to the demanding conditions of life on the Great Plains.

Horned lark

Sand dunes

Chapter

5

IN THE DESERT

Two separate bands—one in the Northern Hemisphere, the other in the Southern Hemisphere—circle the globe, each covering an area whose boundaries begin approximately 15 degrees from the equator and end some 40 degrees from it. Within these warm, sunny belts, long ago named the "horse latitudes" or doldrums, are found the deserts of the world: the Thar of northwest India; the wastelands of Iran and Arabia; the Turkestan of southwest Russia; Asia's Gobi; the Sahara and Kalahari of Africa; 44 percent of the continent of Australia; South America's very, very dry Atacama; and the great deserts of North America. Together these arid lands occupy almost a sixth of the earth's surface, with the Sahara alone accounting for 3,650,000 square miles.

Some people say that the word *desert* includes not only these dry areas, but frozen areas, like the Arctic, and salt-water beaches and marshes as well. Most geographers, however, limit the designation *desert* to regions that receive less than 10 inches of uneven rainfall annually, and have a relatively high mean temperature. For our purposes, we will further limit this discussion to the 500,000 square miles of

North American desert found in the southwestern portion of the United States and the northwestern portion of Mexico.

There are four major deserts on our continent: the Sonoran, trailing from southeastern California into Mexico; the Chihuahuan, stretching from south of the border into Texas and New Mexico; the Mojave, a desert of southern California; and the Great Basin Desert of Utah and Nevada. In addition there are several smaller deserts, including the Painted Desert of Arizona with its terraces of red, yellow, and purple sands and its Petrified Forest, where you can see the stone remains of trees estimated to be 160 million years old.

None of these deserts are, as the name implies, deserted. They once supported a number of thriving Indian civilizations and continue today to support a great variety of plant and animal life. A walk through the desert provides a dramatic demonstration of the stubborn and successful efforts of living things to survive, despite some of the most inhospitable conditions nature has ever devised.

The Making of a Desert

The horse latitudes, so the story goes, were given their name because a great many horses died or were dropped overboard in the seas of these two belts. It was there that the ships carrying the horses to new lands were often halted in their travels by long periods of cloudless and windless weather, the kind of weather that fails to swell sails or bring rain. Lands located in these almost rainless latitudes are dry.

Mountains are another cause of dryness. Standing between deserts and oceans, they block the passage of moisture-laden clouds attempting to climb the peaks. As the clouds rise higher, they become colder and colder, finally dropping their rain before it can reach the mountain's other side. On our continent the barrier is the over-1000-miles-long Sierra Nevada and Cascade ranges. This towering granite blockade effectively separates the moist winds of the Pacific from the thirsty lands beyond.

Ocean currents also contribute to the making of a desert. A cold current like the Oyashio in the Pacific keeps evaporation of ocean water to a minimum, providing prevailing winds with little moisture to carry to southwestern United States and northwestern Mexico.

Some rain, of course, does manage to fall upon the desert, although the driest parts of North America receive less than 2 inches a year. Bagdad, in the Mojave, averages 2.28 inches annually, although one year it had 9.9 inches of rain. It also holds the North American drought record—three virtually rainless years. This erratic pattern is by no means unusual. Irregularity is the only certain feature of rainfall in the deserts throughout the world.

Lack of rain is basic to the desert climate. So is low humidity, although the amount of moisture in the air varies greatly from place to place and from season to season. This relative absence of moisture, plus a scarcity of plant covering, exposes the land to the full heat of the sun. The desert blazes by day, reaching, in North America, some of the highest temperatures ever recorded on earth. A thermometer reading of 134 degrees F, officially reported at Greenland Ranch in Death Valley, California, has been surpassed only once: Azizia, in the Libyan section of the Sahara, reached a scorching 136.4 degrees F.

Summer desert temperatures on our continent regularly go above 100 degrees F. Yet, because much of this heat radiates back into the air, it is quickly dissipated. The mercury may fall at night as much as 70 or 80 degrees F. Desert evenings grow chilly, even in the summer. Winter night temperatures in the Great Basin are often below freezing, accompanied by considerable snow.

In addition to lack of rain, low humidity, and high daytime temperatures, the desert has yet another distinguishing characteristic—its winds. Some of the winds that have unsuccessfully tried to blow rain clouds over the mountains and into the lands beyond reach the desert devoid of moisture. These dry, drying winds dehydrate the soil and hasten evaporation. They also bring about dust storms and sandstorms, spectacular events that blot out the sun and blind the eyes of animal and man. They are responsible, too,

Rainbow Bridge, Utah

for the shuffling of sand that builds the majestic dunes.

The common factors of climate are the unifying elements in any desert description. But these factors do not, by any means, produce a uniform desert appearance. The monotonous, and awesome, vista of thousands upon thousands of miles of endless sands is only one facet of the landscape. There are salt lakes and playas (dry lake beds); brown, hard-packed flatlands and geometric golden dunes. There are badlands—eroded rock and clay surfaces that look like jagged miniature mountains, separated by deep vertical channels. High mountains rise from the desert floor and steep canyons cut below its surface. Natural pillars, arches, pedestals and columns, curved mesas, and weathered buttes provide an impressive collection of sculptured shapes. Burned, blown, eroded, the materials that make up the desert scene have been manipulated in hundreds of different ways, leaving visitors to marvel not at its sameness but at its astounding variety.

Desert Water

No living thing exists without water, although the amount required for survival may be minute. Dry as the desert is, it receives enough water to support plant and animal life.

Rain, the chief water source, gives the desert a bare minimum of moisture. When a storm is short-lived, the sun, winds, and high temperatures cause the swift evaporation of every drop. But even a cloudburst, which may provide the desert with its annual supply of rain in one great outpouring, often fails to replenish the soil moisture. Where the land is hard-baked, the water flows over it instead of penetrating.

When these flowing waters come together in a torrential stream, they gouge deep gullies, called washes or arroyos, in the desert floor. Sweeping along sediment and mud, these torrents flood the land, drowning the plants and animals in their paths.

Arroyo waters eventually evaporate in the hot after-storm air, flow into a river bed, or form a small lake, which will also quickly dry out. But another heavy storm, perhaps a year later, perhaps ten, will fill the arroyos and bring lakes or rivers briefly to life once more.

The other chief source of desert water is the natural oasis—product of a spring, water hole, or river—signaled by an island of fertile green growth. For desert travelers, the oasis is always a welcome sight.

Where water is not naturally available, it is obtained by man's efforts. In the past, Indian desert dwellers dug wells to reach the waters below, or brought it from a distance through canals. Modern techniques have improved well digging and provided pipelines to carry water many hundreds of miles. New irrigation systems also help to supply water to desert regions. But none of these efforts have thus far changed the basic nature of the desert. It is still, for the most part, very dry.

Plant Adaptations

Plants that have adapted themselves to the desert's heat and dryness are called xerophytes—dry plants. Xerophytes have developed a number of ingenious ways of surviving on a meager supply of water.

Most of the small desert annuals avoid the hot periods altogether, remaining in the seed stage until the season of rains. If conditions are unsatisfactory, the seeds, protected by their tough coats, may lie dormant for several years. Eventually, however, they germinate and grow, putting out flamboyant blossoms in purples and pinks, reds and oranges, blues, golds, and whites. During their brief life span, measured in weeks, they bear new seeds, which must now wait a year, or two, or ten before they brighten the desert once more.

While the annuals dodge drought, the perennials

face up to it. Plants such as the whiplike ocotillo are present all year long, but stay dormant until rain stirs them to activity. A wet spell will provoke from the straight, bare, dead-looking ocotillo branches a display of hundreds of tiny green leaves and clusters of fiery red flowers.

Monument Valley, Arizona-Utah

But except for this post-rain bloom, the ocotillo and many other desert plants remain leafless. Leaves are an extravagance in arid lands because they lose so much moisture to the air. Those plants that do not shed them for most of the year may conserve water by turning only the leaf edge, not the entire surface, to the sun. They may put out leaves of diminutive size. They may roll up their leaves during the hot hours of the day. Some have waxy or leathery leaf

Agave or century plant

coats to help prevent evaporation. A hairy covering may provide them with shade.

The agave or century plant of the Chihuahuan Desert has managed to utilize its leaves for the vital task of storing water. Its circle of stiff greenery, growing close to the soil, makes a modest-looking plant for the first ten or fifteen years of its life, after which there appears a tall stalk topped with yellow blossoms.

The cactus family, the most familiar group of plants in the American desert, has eliminated the leaf problem by almost completely eliminating the leaves and turning over many important functions to the stem. One duty of the cactus stem is to manufacture food. Another is to store water. Two champion water storers are the towering saguaro and the pudgy barrel cactus.

The saguaro, Arizona's official state flower, is a high-rising plant whose shallow, widespread roots soak up water by the hundreds of gallons and pass it on for storage in the accordion-pleated, flexible stem. This treelike growth lives as long as 200 years, rises to heights of 50 feet, and bears creamy white blossoms at the tips of its stout stalks. A mature saguaro may weigh 10 tons, 80 percent of which is water.

Saguaro

The flower-crowned barrel cactus, with a shape that justifies its name, is one bright green stem adorned with pink, red, and white thorns. After a rain the fluted, flexible stem wall stretches, allowing the cactus to fill up its "barrel" with large quantities of water.

The century plant and most cactus plants are called succulents, because their water-storing abilities make them juicy. Almost all cactuses use their stems to store water and have fleshy, shallow, spreading roots to take maximum advantage of rainfall. The night-blooming cereus, however, is a dissident member of the cactus family. Its water-storing unit is not the stem, but its huge underground roots, which may weigh as much as 50 pounds.

Desert roots are basically of three types: enlarged storage roots, like those of the cereus; shallow and widespread root systems, like most cactus roots and the roots of the creosote bush; and taproots, which penetrate deep into the ground to seek out water. The taproot of the yucca is 40 feet long. The mesquite, a common desert growth, puts down a taproot 100 feet into the soil.

There seems to be no end to the artful adaptations plants have made in order to survive with little water. Some keep water needs to a minimum by maintaining a dwarf form throughout their lifetime. Others combat drought by dying back to the ground. The barbs, spines, spurs, spikes, and prickles with which a large number of desert plants are armed may also be considered adaptations to aridity. According to one theory, these thorny weapons are intended to discourage browsing animals from nibbling away the foliage produced at such great effort in the dry climate. Other botanists think that their function is to provide plants with a latticework of shade.

As you have seen in the desert, almost every plant submits to the facts of life in this drink-or-drought world, asking for little water, trying to get by on less. In response to the gift of rain, however, they fill the

Joshua tree

dry, brown lands with flowers and fruits in colors beyond belief, a sight well worth hundreds of thirsty days and nights.

Common Desert Plants

Thousands of different kinds of plants are responsible for the striking display of color in the desert. We can look at only a few—a sample of those most commonly found in North America's arid lands.

The brilliant, brief-blooming annuals give their finest performance in the spring, when they appear to blanket the desert as far as the eye can see. Dunes swarm with fragrant lavender verbena, and masses of golden California poppies gleam in the sun. Various

Yucca

evening primroses abound in many parts of the Southwest, their yellow, white, or pink flowers filling the air with sweet scents. In low, hot washes and the canyons of warm deserts grows the sand blazing-star, with creamy, crimson-centered flowers and leaves covered with stiff hairs. The emory rock daisy sprouts on the sides of canyons and rocky hills, displaying a bright white flower and vivid green foliage.

Other desert wildflowers include the prickly poppy, a thistlelike plant with cup-shaped white blooms brightly punctuated with orange stamens; the stunning globe mallow, a perennial whose large flowers range from reddish-purple to pale lavender and apricot yellow; the blue-violet wild hyacinths and heliotropes; and the ghost flower, with its purple-dotted pale yellow face. Look, too, for the carmine-colored penstemon, a long-stemmed, graceful perennial whose blossoms faintly resemble snapdragons, and the evil-smelling, narcotic Jimson weed, with gorgeous trumpet-shaped flowers in the white to lavender range.

Many beautiful and unusual trees and shrubs can be found on the desert. One of the most striking is the 30-foot-tall Joshua tree, which has shaggy branches tipped with white flower clusters and sharp teeth at the edges of its leaves. The Joshua tree is an indicator plant—a plant that marks the boundaries—of the Mojave Desert. A National Monument in southern California has been set aside for its preservation and exhibition.

The Joshua tree is a type of yucca. Another type is the soaptree yucca, state flower of New Mexico. Ranging from 3 to 20 feet in height, the soaptree bears waxy white blossoms. Its roots have long served as a soap substitute.

The soaptree yucca belongs to the lily family, but its needle-pointed leaves give it a palmy appearance. The sotol is another palmlike plant of the American desert. It is also a yucca member of the lily family. Hundreds of ribbonlike leaves—gray-green, strap-shaped, prickly—grow from its short trunk. Emerging from the leaves is a 7-or-8-foot-tall flower stalk, bearing a plume of small, white blossoms.

The mesquite, a member of the pea and bean family, varies from a small bush to a good-sized tree. Its leaves are green and shiny, its blossoms are yellow-green, and its wood makes excellent firewood. This thorny plant may be found along the desert's dry arroyos and on the dunes. In some places it grows in dense groves.

The yellow-flowered catclaw is another member of the pea family. Its seeds, like those of the mesquite, can be roasted, ground, and eaten. This plant gets its name from its stout, curved spines, which resemble the claws of a cat.

The desert ironwood belongs to the pea family

Organ-pipe cactus

too. Its wood is extremely hard; its flowers are small and purple; and it wears, except in the driest periods, a covering of gray-green foliage. The seedpods of this handsome, bushy tree have a peanutlike taste.

The jojoba plant also has tasty nuts, and its gray-green leathery leaves, set on widespread branches, are edible too.

The hackberry is a thorny, 3-to-10-foot evergreen whose small, red fruit supports wildlife.

The flaming red blossoms of the ocotillo provide a meal for the desert mule deer, and the brittlebush, with its vivid yellow flowers, is a favorite food of deer and mountain sheep.

The heart of the agave, roasted and fermented, is the source of the intoxicating tequila and mescal.

Cholla cactus

An outstanding beauty is the paloverde, which flourishes in the Sonoran Desert. This tree reaches heights of 15 to 25 feet and has green branches and leaves. In the spring it produces masses of tiny yellow flowers.

Other desert trees to look for are the 100-foot-tall cottonwood, a wide-spreading tree with bright green triangular-shaped leaves, growing along arroyos or streams; the white-barked Arizona sycamore, found in mountain canyons; and the desert willow, actually a member of the begonia family, which bears scented, purple-pink flowers.

The most common desert shrubs are the creosote bushes, from which emanates a strange odor particularly noticeable after a rain. Creosotes are black-limbed with yellow flowers and green, shiny leaves.

The cactuses are a specialty of the American desert, which has produced 1700 species in a variety of intriguing shapes. Most widespread of the giant cactuses is the columnar saguaro, indicator plant of the Sonoran Desert. The organ-pipe cactus is another desert giant, growing up to 25 feet and giving the appearance of an organ with fluted pipes. Its flowers are purple, maroon, or greenish-white and its red, fleshy fruit is edible. Arizona is the home of both the Saguaro National Monument and the Organ Pipe National Monument, established to preserve these impressive plants.

The opuntias are a large group of cactuses which include cylindrical-branched and flat-branched plants. Among the chollas (the cylindrical-branched cactuses) are the jumping cholla, a stocky, straw-colored plant whose little barbed projections break off easily and stick tenaciously to animal and human passersby. The branches have a candelabra effect and the green fruits hang in grapelike clusters. The staghorn cholla is an attractive plant growing up to 12 feet, with flowers in browns, oranges, greens, yellows, or reds. The teddy bear cholla is a cuddly-looking plant with ferocious spines.

The prickly pears are the flat-branched opuntias.

These include the beaver tail cactus, which has small, purple-pink flowers, and the common Engelmann prickly pear, which has long spines, large yellow flowers, and red-purple fruit.

Other common cactuses include the barrel cactus, which provides thirsty travelers with liquid if they can bear the taste; the rainbow cactus, which has morning-glory-shaped blossoms with purple-pink-red petals; and the pincushion cactus, with pink-purple flowers, red fruit, and spines radiating from the stems like pins stuck in a cushion.

One of the glorious experiences in the desert is the sight of the night-blooming cereus in bloom. Plain-looking most of the time, this cactus displays—for only one month, and only after dark—huge blossoms of dazzling whiteness and overpowering fragance. Admiring Mexicans have named it Queen of the Night.

The desert even has grasses, many of which serve as food for grazing cattle. Together with the wildflowers, trees, shrubs, and cactuses, they provide a surprisingly generous covering in these far-from-deserted lands of North America.

Animal Adaptations

Desert animals, like desert plants, have had to adapt to the rigors of desert life. In response to high temperatures and low water supplies, living creatures have developed modifications of structure and habit that enable them to make their homes in the hottest, driest lands in the world.

One almost-universal habit of birds and mammals is to avoid the sun during the burning hours of the day. Desert animals have no special resistance to the cruel heat, and so they cease their activities when the sun is high. Retreating to underground burrows or the shelter of a bush or rock, they do not emerge until the cool of evening, night, or early morning.

Some animals elude the heat not for hours, but for months. In time of drought, the spade-foot toad

Desert bighorn

Peccary

Ringtail cat

digs itself a cell and retires into a state of suspended animation for about three-quarters of a year. This period of estivation, as it is called, ends when heavy rainfall awakens the sluggish amphibian.

A few creatures cope with desert conditions the way annuals do—by lying dormant until the water supply is sufficient. Bees will remain in the pupa stage until moisture stimulates their development, even if that takes several years. In very dry areas the span between the laying and hatching of shrimp eggs may be a quarter of a century. Another plantlike habit practiced by certain desert animals is the hoarding of water. The desert tortoise stores it in two sacs located in its upper shell.

The skins of some animals are particularly well suited for protection against loss of water. Spiders, scorpions, and centipedes, for instance, have dense body covers. Reptiles are guarded by their scales. Almost all desert inhabitants have lighter-colored skins than their family members in cooler climates. The pale color reflects more heat and helps conserve moisture.

Even the processes of elimination are geared to desert conditions. To avoid discarding water, lizards and snakes expell urine as well as feces in almost solid form.

A few desert animals are actually able to survive without an external water supply—by manufacturing water inside their own bodies. The kangaroo rat is the most famous desert water maker, combining oxygen and hydrogen from its food to produce the vital fluid. The powder-post beetle is another creature that goes through life without taking a drink.

Desert animals not only must deal with problems of heat and moisture but with the many inconveniences brought about by the hot, clogging, slippery sand. Many creatures dig underground retreats to hide away from sandstorms. Long lashes, hair inside ears, nose valves that can, when necessary, close—all are ways of holding off the irritating grains. The ridges along the abdomens of snakes improve traction.

As you can see, animals show as much ingenuity as plants in their efforts to get along under desert conditions. Tenaciously making a place for themselves in this rugged atmosphere, they offer excellent lessons in survival for the most sophisticated members of their kingdom.

Desert Mammals

The mammals of the desert range in size from the bighorn sheep, weighing up to 350 pounds, to the 3-inch (tail included) desert shrew.

The bighorn has been seen in the mountains, while deer relations of the desert's Sonora whitetail and Mexican mule deer will be seen in the forest. The Mexican pronghorn antelope, which roams the border, closely resembles its northern relation, the American pronghorn—found on the plains.

The piglike collared peccary has short legs, thick neck, long snout, and razor-sharp tusks. One of the larger desert mammals, it stands 20 inches at the shoulder and may weigh up to 60 pounds. The peccary's salt-and-pepper body is marked with a lighter-colored collar of bristles on the front of its shoulders and a row of stiff, dark hackles along its back. A musk gland at the rear emits a pungent odor that carries quite a distance.

The wide-ranging bobcat is a dark-spotted tawny brown, with long legs, small, tufted ears, and a handsome cat face. Its head and body measure between 25 and 30 inches, and a black-tipped tail adds another 5 inches to its length.

One of the prettiest desert mammals is the ring-tailed cat, a relative of the raccoon. Half of its 30-inch length is tail, decorated with distinctive bands of brownish-black and white. It stands on short legs, listens through large ears, and shyly surveys the world through big, black-ringed eyes.

Smallest and most graceful of the foxes is the kit or desert fox, rarely more than 3 feet in total length. Its coat is sandy yellow, and its long, bushy tail is tipped with black. The kit has piercing dark eyes, and huge ears to hear the scampering of its prey in the desert night.

The husky burrowing badger is a powerful digger with short ears, neck, tail, and legs. You have met this desert dweller on the plains.

Desert skunks include the common striped skunk and the little spotted skunk, marked with stripes and dots of white, which we will also see in the forest. There is another interesting variety called the hooded skunk, which has a hood or cape of long and usually white hairs on its head and neck.

The high-jumping rabbits are represented by the black-tailed jackrabbit, gray-brown with large, black-tipped ears and a streak of black on its tail, and the antelope jackrabbit, with a fawn-colored body and white-rimmed eyes and ears. The Arizona cottontail is soft-furred, pale-gray, and fluffy-tailed.

The spiny pocket mouse gets its name from the fur-lined pouches it wears on the outside of its cheeks. This brown desert dweller is about 8 inches from nose to tip of tail.

The southern grasshopper mouse wears a bright tawny coat. Its 4-inch total length is 50 percent tail.

The desert kangaroo rat also wears cheek pouches, which it uses to transport dry seeds. This unusual rodent has two very special characteristics. One is its ability to get along without drinking water. The other is its kangaroo-like habit of jumping, holding its short front legs out of the way, and using only its long hind legs and tail. The function of the long, tip-tufted tail is to help maintain balance during the rodent's great 8-foot (or longer) leaps.

Bats, the only flying mammals, are plentiful in the desert. Each summer evening fifteen or twenty species can be seen at Carlsbad Caverns National Park, where they swarm from the cavern entrance in huge numbers to search for food.

Desert fox

Kangaroo rat

Desert Reptiles

Seemingly oblivious to the fierce heat, lizards appear in the desert by day, stalking their dinner or basking in the glowing sun. They do, however, have their limits of toleration, returning to the shade when the thermometer moves in the neighborhood of 110 degrees F.

The United States has only one poisonous lizard—the Gila monster, with a head-body length of 12 to 16 inches and a tail one half to one third that measurement. Its nerve-affecting venom is secreted by glands located in the lower jaw and passed into wounds made by the teeth. The beaded, patterned back of this heavy animal is yellow or orange, marked with brownish black.

The chuckwalla is a big—16 inches in all—scaly lizard, second only to the Gila monster in size. It is well known for a unique protective device: When an enemy tries to remove the chuckwalla from its rocky hide-out, this lizard fills its lungs with air, inflating its body until it becomes unremovably wedged in place.

The gentle banded gecko, only 4 to 6 inches long, is pale yellow-gray with reddish-brown spots or bands. It looks something like a salamander. Unlike other North American desert lizards, which make only a hissing sound, the gecko squeaks protestingly in a high-pitched voice when disturbed.

The desert spiny lizard is 3½ to 5½ inches in head-body length, yellow to yellow-brown above with dusky crossbands or spots, and black marks on the shoulders. The male has a blue throat patch and other blue markings.

The collared lizard has two well-pronounced black bands, separated by white, at its neck. Its tail is twice as long as its 3¼-to-4½-inch head-body measurement.

The speedy zebra-tailed lizard (2½ to 3½ inches in head-body length) is light-colored with a handsome black-and-white-marked tail. It is one of our fastest reptiles, sometimes achieving speeds of 18 miles per hour.

The desert horned toad, which is really a lizard too, is small, flat, and round-bodied, with a short tail and spines or horns around the collar. Head-body length is 2¾ to 3¾ inches. In cloudy weather this lizard nose-dives into the sand and remains concealed until the sun appears again.

In another reptile category is the desert tortoise, with stocky limbs and a high-arched back. It measures some 13 inches in length. This famous water hoarder is reputed never to take a drink, getting all the water it needs from juicy plants, storing the water in sacs, and moving slowly and infrequently to keep its water requirements to a minimum.

The snakes, night hunters of the desert, are much less plentiful than the lizards. If you exercise reasonable caution, you can take your walk without fear of harm from these essentially shy reptiles.

Gila monster

Many species of rattlesnakes live in the arid lands. All are venomous. Included among the rattlers is the sidewinder, which wears horny plates over each eye, ranges between 18 and 24 inches in length, and gets its name from its looping sideways method of moving along the loose sand. The western diamondback rattlesnake, which we also saw in the mountains, is considerably larger.

The coral snake, relative of the cobra, is also venomous. Pretty red, white, and black bands encircle the body of this slender 20-to-30-incher.

Chuckwalla

The racers and whipsnakes are about 4 or 5 feet long, thin-bodied, and active. One desert representative is the red racer, colored in red- or yellow-brown with black markings.

A V-shaped scale extends over the nose of the 12-to-20-inch spotted leaf-nosed snake, a large-eyed reptile with dark blotches on its tan, pink or gray-brown back. A beige tip marks the nose of the 2-to-3-foot long-nosed snake, an excellent burrower that wears black patches on its back.

The Arizona bullsnake averages 5 feet. It is basically yellow with a thick mottling of brownish blotches. The Arizona kingsnake, about 3 feet long, has a shiny jet body patterned attractively with white ovals.

Horned toad

Desert Insects and Other Arthropods

A large number of insects populate the desert, appearing chiefly in the warmer weather. Most common are the grasshoppers, which include the robust lubber. One type of desert lubber has a gray-brown body and dark-spotted, short front wings.

Butterflies and moths are the second most common desert insect group. Huge numbers of painted ladies—a butterfly found all over the world—decorate

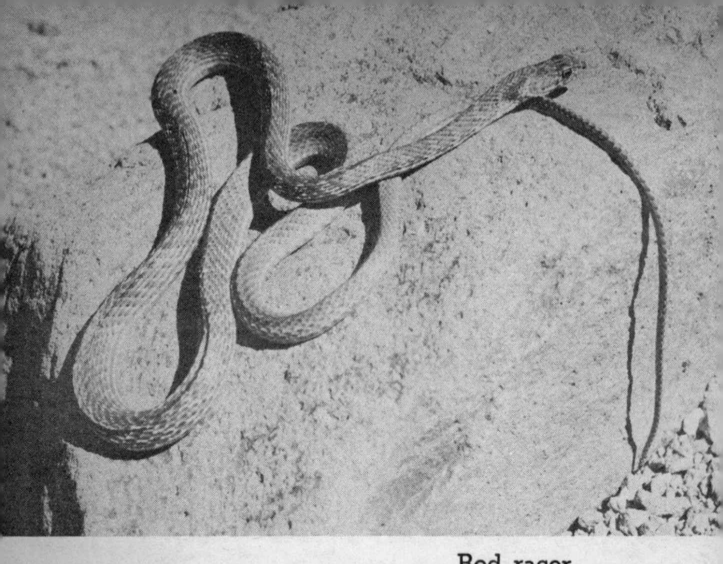

Red racer

the desert with their reds, blacks, whites, browns, and blues. Representatives of the attractive swift-flying sphinx moth family congregate in great crowds in the Sonoran Desert.

Third in numbers are the desert's beetles, and its wasps, bees, and ants.

The unique powder-post beetle family has desert representatives. This $\frac{1}{4}$-inch red-brown elongated insect leaves a trail of powder behind as it tunnels into dead, dry tree trunks, dining on the wood and converting part of it into water.

The beautiful tarantula wasp, also called the tarantula hawk, has wings in shades of orange or red. It preys on tarantulas, first stinging and paralyzing them, then placing them in its burrow as food for its young.

Other desert arthropods include centipedes and millipedes, which we will see on our forest walk, spiders, and scorpions.

The wolf spider, which is found in damp fields and woods as well as in the desert, is a hairy, medium-to-large spider with strong legs. Its eight eyes are arranged in three rows—two rows of two large eyes apiece, one row of four small eyes. This spider spins no web but hunts by running down its prey. Until the young can fend for themselves, the mother wolf spider carries them on her back.

Another desert spider is *Eurypelma californicum,* largest of this country's tarantulas. Its dark-brown body, covered with rust-colored hairs, is about 2 inches long, and its size and hairiness give it an alarming appearance. Despite its bad reputation, the tarantula's bite is not toxic to man.

Beware the black widow, however. It only bites when provoked, but the bite is venomous. You can identify the female by the crimson hourglass design on the underside of her abdomen. The rest of the body is velvety black.

Scorpions are plentiful in southwestern United States. They have two large pinchers, and an abdomen that ends in a taillike section tipped with an armed stinger. Only two species of desert scorpions have a deadly sting. Both are small, slender, and straw-colored.

Whip scorpions are also found in the desert. Unlike true scorpions, these rust-colored arthropods have no stinger. They are, however, equipped with spiny pinchers.

Lubber grasshopper

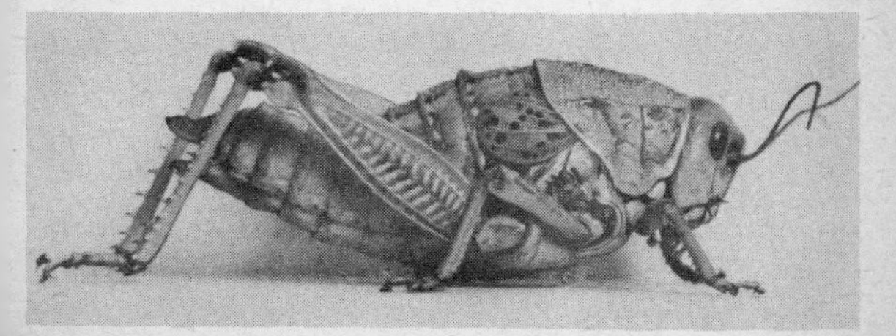

Desert Birds

The birds of the desert may be permanent dwellers or part-time residents. Colorful and plentiful, they are easily identified against the stark, thin-foliaged scenery.

The roadrunner, a cuckoo that travels by foot, is a comical-looking creature with a long, maneuverable, white-tipped tail shooting out from its body at an insouciant angle. It is slender and heavily streaked, with strong legs, a shaggy crest, and short, rounded wings.

The elf owl hides in the woodpecker holes of the saguaro cactus by day, but can be located at night by its distinctive call—a rapid yipping, whining, puppylike sound. This diminutive bird is small-headed and earless, with white "eyebrows" and rust-colored stripes on its underparts.

A black plume curves from the head of the pretty Gambel's quail, and the male's face and throat are patterned in black and white. The scaled quail, pale-gray in color, has a bushy white crest. Its name comes from the scaly markings on breast and back.

Among the desert members of the woodpecker family is the gilded flicker, which has a yellow lining on wings and tail. The male displays a red "mustache." This flicker nests in saguaro holes, as does the Gila woodpecker, which wears a white wing patch and zebra stripes down its back. The ladder-backed woodpecker has black-and-white stripes on back and face. Males have red caps.

Desert representatives of the flycatcher family are the vermilion flycatcher, Say's phoebe, the ash-throated flycatcher, and the phainopepla. The male vermilion flycatcher has vivid scarlet coloring on crown, throat, and underparts, with upper parts and tail brown to black. Say's phoebe is large and pale, with rusty underparts and a black tail. The ash-throated flycatcher is medium-sized, with a slightly bushy head, two white wing bars, a whitish throat, and pale yellow belly. The phainopepla is a silky flycatcher. Males are slim and glossy black with patches of white on the wings.

A pale bird with contrasting dark eyes and dark tail is Le Conte's thrasher. The crissal thrasher has yellowish eyes, a deep chestnut patch under the tail, and a decidedly curved bill.

The cactus wren, larger than other North American wrens, sounds a one-pitch *chug-chug-chug-chug-chug,* unbirdlike and quite monotonous. It has a heavily spotted breast and a white stripe over the eye.

The black-tailed gnatcatcher looks like a mockingbird in miniature. It has blue-gray upper parts and the male wears a black cap during the breeding season.

A jet-black throat and white face stripes distinguish the black-throated or desert sparrow. This pretty bird has a gray body with white underparts.

The hummingbird family also has desert representatives. The male Costa's hummingbird has an amethyst throat and crown. The relatively large violet-crowned hummingbird has a white throat and underparts, and a black-tipped red bill. Only the male's crown is violet; the female's is a dull green-blue. The broad-billed hummingbird is dark green, with a blue throat for the males and pearly gray for the ladies. Both sexes have red bills.

The white-necked raven, often a gregarious bird, sounds a flat, hoarse *kraak.* White punctuates the neck and breast of this dweller of the mesquite flats and yucca deserts.

Other birds to watch for are the pyrrhuloxia, a crested gray and red bird with a parrotlike bill; the small gray verdin with its yellow head; Scott's oriole, distinguished from other United States orioles by its solid black head; and the pale, scaly Inca dove with its square-ended tail.

Many other birds are likely to be encountered on your walk—among them several wide-ranging species like the caracara, loggerhead shrike, turkey vulture, and golden eagle. Although these are not specifically desert birds, do not be surprised if you see a shrike

Cactus wren

wearing a black mask, or glimpse a flash of gold as an eagle wheels overhead.

End of the Journey

At some point during your desert travels you will probably come across a gleaming sea complete with rippling waves. But this inviting vision vanishes at your approach, for it is nothing more than a mirage caused by the bending and refraction of light rays. All your eyes see, really, is a piece of blue sky temporarily laid at your feet.

There are no seas in these dry lands of North America, but we expect that the natural wonders that do exist are enough to fully occupy your senses. Those we pointed out are among the representative features that make a desert a desert—arid and alien and, in its own way, very beautiful indeed.

Lodgepole pine

Chapter 6

IN THE FOREST

DESPITE man's relentless assaults on the forests of his planet, there are still 9.6 billion acres of forest land. In the forty-eight adjacent states and coastal Alaska, a third of the land area is wooded, providing us with a tree-ruled realm of 664 million acres.

There are many ways to subdivide the forests of contiguous United States, but we shall consider them as four great belts. One is a towering coniferous, softwood forest that follows the Pacific Coast from western Alaska to central California. A second coniferous band lies astride the Cascade and Sierra ranges, and a third climbs the Rockies from Canada to Mexico. The fourth, a great forest dominated in much of the North by hardwoods and in the southern states by pines, blankets the eastern half of the country.

Forest Trees

As you walk through these forests you will see a profusion of growing things—mosses and ferns and fungi, wildflowers and shrubs. But the pillars of the community are, indisputably, the trees—the evergreens (including most conifers and a few that are not cone-bearers), which remain verdant all the year round, and the broad-leaved deciduous trees (most hardwoods and a few softwoods), which adapt to the drought of winter by shedding their leaves.

Most forest trees have the same requirements for survival—a favorable growing season and a minimum of 15 inches of annual rainfall. Almost as important as the amount of moisture is the timing of its distribution.

In parts of the northern Pacific Coast moist winds dump an average of 100 inches of rain in each year, with a generous portion falling during the growing season. The result is a luxuriant forest of western hemlocks, Sitka spruces, western red cedars, Douglas firs, and silver firs.

Farther south, in northern and central California, the heavy rains fall in the wintertime. But here moisture is provided during the growing season by thick summer fogs that roll in from the ocean, fostering the growth of dense redwood forests within a strip of land more than 400 miles long and usually no farther than 20 miles from the ocean.

In southern California and northern Mexico, the coast receives an adequate amount of annual rainfall. But because it occurs in the winter instead of in the growing season, summer conditions are dry and desertlike. All you will find here is the unimpressive shrubbery of chaparral.

The dignified and massive western hemlock, largest of eight hemlock species, achieves average heights of 130 to 150 feet.[1] Its flat, lustrous green leaves are rounded at the ends and distinctively grooved. Clay-brown cones, pointed and pendent, hang from the branchlets on short, threadlike stems.

Largest of the spruces on this continent, the north Pacific's Sitka spruce climbs from a swollen, buttressed base to occasional heights of over 280 feet, though it ordinarily averages 80 to 125. The thick,

[1] Most tree heights given here are averages, not maximums.

Douglas fir

Silver fir

flat needles, growing on smooth stems, are bright blue-green and pointed. Flexible yellow or red-brown cones tip the pendulous branches.

Look for the western red cedar from southern Alaska to northern California, where it grows to average heights of 150 to 175 feet. Leathery brown cones are displayed on flattened, lacy leaf sprays that are scalelike and glossy green. Be sure to sniff the delightful scents given off by these leaves. Pieces of the wood are also aromatic.

The Douglas fir, which we shall also see in the Sierras and the Rockies, achieves its noblest state in Washington's and Oregon's coastal ranges. Some of the larger trees, perhaps 1000 years old, reach record heights of 325 feet. Branches are covered with soft, flattened, slightly pointed needles that display pendulous oval cones with three-pointed bracts extending beyond each scale.

Named for the silvery-white underside of its needles, the beautiful silver fir lifts its head 200 feet into the sky. In open woods this spire-shaped coni-

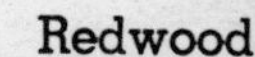

Redwood

fer wears rather short but graceful branches that sweep down and out, displaying grooved needles dark green on the upper surface. Particularly eye-catching are this fir's oblong purple cones, which measure 3½ to 6 inches long.

Now it is time to walk down the Avenue of the Giants, a 100-mile stretch of unbroken forest that represents the heart of redwood country. Beneath your feet lies a thick mat of needles and moss; above your head rise the tallest trees in America.

The redwood, a type of sequoia, has a straight, slightly tapered trunk, which is heavily buttressed. Its open round-topped crown exhibits relatively short, downward-tilted branches. On the lower arms bright yellow-green pointed leaves stick out stiffly, while on the main branches they overlap and have a scalelike appearance. The height record of the redwood is 368 feet; its greatest age is given as 2171 years. In interesting contrast, the purple-brown cones of this king-size tree are smaller than those of any western conifer.

The chaparral community south of the redwood belt is a collection of scrubby plants. This desertlike vegetation is extremely flammable and fires regularly occur in summertime. The typical chaparral has multiple stiff branches, a large and deep root system, and evergreen leaves that are small, hard, and flat.

Chaparral is also found in the foothills of the Sierra Nevadas, which display horizontal bands of trees arranged in a series of life zones from base to summit. Up beyond the chaparral is a western pine belt, followed by a lodgepole pine and red fir belt and, finally, a sparsely forested subalpine belt that reaches to the timberline. Ponderosa pine, formerly called western yellow pine, ranges from 150 to 230 feet in height. Its short, upturned branches form a spirelike or flat-topped crown. Long, dark yellow-green needles grow in tufts on the ends of the branchlets, which display red-brown cones near the tips. This pine is the most common and most widely distributed of the western conifers.

Other conifers of the western pine belt are the Douglas fir; the massive, heavily foliaged white fir, named for the light color of its bark and plump, blunt needles; the sugar pine, tallest of the pines at record heights of 245 feet; and the 3400-year-old giant sequoia, found in isolated groves on the Sierra's western slopes.

Towering over its neighbors, the giant sequoia stands 300 to 330 feet high. The bright foliage, deep green in color, has a scalelike appearance, with sharp-pointed leaves overlapping one another on the branches. Cones are woody, egg-shaped, and yellow-brown. One look at this great and ancient tree and you will understand why naturalist John Muir called it "king of all the conifers in the world."

The next life zone of the Sierras displays dense forests of stately red fir, a 60-to-125-foot symmetrical tree with a narrow, cone-shaped crown. The dark green-blue needles have blunt ends, and oval purple-brown cones stand erect on the branches.

Also in this zone are lodgepole, Jeffrey, and silver pines. Lodgepole pine is usually 60 to 80 feet high and has paired bright yellow-green needles and glossy yellow-brown cones. Jeffrey pine bears a close resemblance to ponderosa pine but its needles are bluish-green and its big thick cones, 5 to 15 inches long, are much larger than the ponderosa's 3-to-6-inch cones. Silver pine, also called western white pine, averages 90 to 110 feet and has pale blue-green needles growing in bunches of five, and slender, cylindrical cones.

Lodgepole pine is also found in the subalpine belt, growing shorter as it climbs higher. Its companions near the timberline are whitebark and foxtail pines.

The sturdy whitebark ranges in height from 40 feet to a dwarfed 6 feet where it is buffeted by interminable winds. Thick and squatty with short, flexible limbs, this pine wears long, rigid needles, grouped in fives, and small purple-brown cones that are almost stemless.

The foxtail or bristlecone pine stands between

Bristlecone pine

35 and 40 feet in good locations, but is merely a twisted shrub at very high elevations. Deep-green needles grow in bundles of five, clustering densely at the branch ends to form tufts that resemble foxes' tails. The cones are chocolate-brown and display a sharp, curved prickle on each scale. The bristlecone is recognized as the oldest living thing in the world at plus-4000 years.

The winds that water the forests of the Far West are wrung dry by the time they cross the Sierras. Beyond these mountains the land is arid. But as the winds travel east they pick up moisture again, accumulating enough to support the trees of the Rockies.

You will see only tundra plants on the highest peaks of the Rocky Mountains, but below the timberline Engelmann spruce appears. This tree has soft, flexible needles of a deep blue-green, light-brown 1-to-3-inch cones, and a scaly trunk with a bark of russet red. Averaging 80 to 110 feet in height, Engelmanns may grow as short as 2 to 4 feet when exposed to the cold and wind of the higher slopes.

In parts of its range the Engelmann spruce is joined by alpine fir, western larch, whitebark pine, and bristlecone pine.

You will recognize the alpine fir by its distinctive spire, rising to a slender tip on this 60-to-90-foot tree. The deep blue-green needles, long and flat on the lower branches, shorter and thicker on the higher branches, are massed and upward pointing. A silver resin drips from upright purple cones.

Western larch, largest and most important of the larches, sometimes stands more than 200 feet tall. This sparse-foliaged conifer bears elongated cones and pale-green needles in bundles of thirty to forty. The larches (and the southern cypress) are the only conifers that shed their leaves.

Below the spruce zone are forests of Douglas fir, and lower still the fir is mixed with ponderosa pine. Next comes a woodland of Utah juniper (usually only 6 to 12 feet high, with pale yellow-green needles) and pinyon pine (low and round-headed with paired yellow-green needles and yellow-brown egg-shaped cones.) These yield, at the base, to eastward spreading grasslands.

Moisture for the forests of the East is carried by winds moving inland from the Great Lakes, the Gulf of Mexico, and the Atlantic Ocean. Within this heavily forested region, which covers almost the entire eastern half of the United States, is a coastal-plain woods of pine—pitch, shortleaf, loblolly, longleaf, and slash—and a southern Florida community of exotic tropical trees. But we will look now at some of the familiar and important deciduous trees that dominate the scenery of the eastern forests, whether bare-branched in winter, green-leaved in spring and summer, or blazing with autumn's red and gold.

In the northern and central portion of the eastern forests are many oaks, including black, white, and northern red. Three other important oaks—the southern red, the live, and the swamp chestnut—are found in the south Atlantic and Gulf states.

The black oak is one of the biggest and most common eastern oaks, averaging 60 to 80 feet tall with a wide-spreading crown of smooth, dark-green bristle-tipped leaves. About the same height is the striking white oak, with glossy leaves, wide-spreading branches, and a light-colored bark for which it was probably named. The 70-to-90-foot northern red oak displays a symmetrical crown of dark-green foliage spreading from a short, stout trunk. The 70-to-80-foot southern red oak has firm and glossy dark-green leaves, some bell-like and some finger-like. The 50-foot live oak, so named because it retains its leaves throughout the year, is a majestic round-headed tree with a massive, buttressed trunk and long, spreading limbs. The swamp chestnut oak, 60 to 80 feet, has shiny green leaves with toothed margins. All oaks bear acorns—a fruit exclusive to these trees—and have simple, alternate leaves. Except for the evergreen live oak, those mentioned here are deciduous.

Birches have simple, alternate leaves whose margins are toothed and sometimes lobed. Look for yel-

White oak

American elm

low, paper, sweet, and gray birches in the north.

Yellow birch has silver-yellow bark, conelike fruit, and dull, dark-green leaves that are yellow-green below. Paper birch is beautifully dressed in cream-white bark and bright-green leaves. Sweet or black birch has almost black bark, slender branches, and dark-green oval-shaped leaves. All are between 60 and 80 feet tall. Gray birch, only 20 to 30 feet high, has a narrow crown, short, slender branches, and thin, triangular leaves.

Other important hardwoods, common to both the northern and central forests of the East, are the American elm, sugar and red maples, beech, shagbark hickory, black walnut, and yellow poplar.

Dignified and vase-shaped, the American elm is the largest and most important elm in eastern North America. It stands 80 to 100 feet high, and its trunk divides to form a broadened crown. If you examine the simple, alternate, toothed leaves, sharply pointed

Sugar maple

at the tip, you will find that they are always lop-sided.

The maple tree is usually distinguished by lobed leaves—simple and opposite—and by fruit that is shaped like a pair of slender wings. The sugar maple is 70 to 130 feet tall. Its dark-green leaves are displayed in a compact, globular crown. The red maple, 60 to 90 feet tall, has bright-green leaves, smooth above and hairy below.

Standing as tall as 120 feet, the beech tree wears a smooth-fitting blue-gray bark. The glossy leaves, simple, alternate, and blue-green, are marked with parallel veins radiating outward to marginal teeth.

The shagbark hickory, a tree of 120 to 140 feet, has an irregular, round-topped crown and alternate compound leaves. Each leaf is composed of a stalk to which are attached five to seven leaflets, narrow at the base, wide at the top, toothed on the margins.

Commonly reaching heights of 100 feet, the black walnut displays stout branches and compound leaves. Some 15 to 23 leaflets, lance-shaped and sharp-toothed, are attached to each somewhat-hairy leaf stem.

Beech

The yellow poplar, also known as the tulip tree, is actually a member of the magnolia family. Its simple, alternate leaves are easily identifiable—broad-based, somewhat like a keystone in outline, usually with four lobes and a broadly notched or indented summit. This tree occasionally attains heights of over 150 feet.

The southern forests also have American elm, beech, and red maple. And they have, in common with the central forest, sycamore and sweet gum.

Most massive of the American hardwoods is the sycamore, with a wide, buttressed trunk, glistening white bark, and simple, alternate leaves that are bright green above and pale below. This tree averages 60 to 120 feet in height.

Sweet gum, named for the fragrant liquid that exudes from its bark, is also called red gum in tribute to its brilliant autumn coloring. Averaging heights of 80 to 120 feet, this tree has still another name—the star-leaved gum. This refers to the shape of the five or seven pointed alternate leaves, glossy-green and aromatic.

Forest Mammals

Except at the edge of the sea, mammals appear importantly in all environments, as they will again in the forest. Mammals are warm-blooded creatures with highly developed brains, particularly the centers of memory and intelligence. They are, with few exceptions, capable of giving birth to living young, nursing them, and providing them with a long period of postnatal training and care.

Mammals occupy almost every kind of habitat, for they are able to burrow, climb, swing by the arms, swim, run, and fly. They are comprised of approximately 5000 to 8000 species, grouped in a number of distinct categories.

Ungulates, which include almost all the larger herbivores, form one major group, separated into odd-toed ungulates (perissodactyls) and even-toed ungulates (artiodactyls). The odd-toed consist of horses and their relatives, tapirs and rhinoceroses, and two extinct groups, the titanotheres and the chalicotheres. The even-toed include pigs and their relatives, and cud-chewers or ruminants (camels, llamas, mouse-deer, deer, giraffes, pronghorns, bison, sheep, goats, and antelopes). In addition, there are subungulates, which include the rodentlike conies of Africa and Syria, the sea cows, and the proboscidians (mammals with trunks), whose only living representative is the elephant. Other ungulates have developed in South America.

The carnivores form another major mammalian group. There are the cats and their relatives (civets, hyenas, cougars, bobcats, lions, tigers, etc.); the dogs and their relatives (weasels, skunks, badgers, otters, raccoons, bears, wolves, foxes); and marine carnivores (seals, sea lions, and walruses).

Besides ungulates and carnivores there are a variety of other mammalian forms: the gnawing rodents (squirrels, beavers, rats, mice, porcupines, guinea pigs, and others), the most flourishing of all mammals; the hares and rabbits, also gnawers; bats, the only air-borne mammals; whales, porpoises, and dolphins; primates, which include tree shrews, lemurs, tarsiers, monkeys, apes, and man; and edentates, "toothless" mammals centered chiefly in South America.

Representatives of many of these mammalian groups can be seen in the forest.

The fleet-footed deer is a typical forest mammal, although members of this vegetarian family actually live in many sorts of environments in many parts of the world. All male deer (and some female deer) wear antlers, bony branching structures that are discarded and replaced once a year.

Heavily concentrated in the woods of the northeast is our most common deer, the white-tailed, with at least five million representatives in the United States. A handsome creature, the whitetail is named for the conspicuous white hair on the underside of its bushy tail, which is carried aloft like a flag in time of danger. During the winter the whitetail wears a grayish coat; in summer its coat is lighter and tawny-colored. Whatever the season, throat and underparts are white. The size of this deer ranges greatly—from 50 to 400 pounds, and from 2 to 3¾ feet in shoulder height. Each antler is composed of a single main beam with two or more erect, unbranched tines.

The black-tailed deer, a small subspecies of the mule deer, rarely weighing more than 150 pounds, dwells in the forests of the West Coast. You can distinguish it from the whitetail in several ways: Its ears are big and black-fringed, its tail—held straight out

White-tailed deer

Red fox

Gray fox

in flight—is black above, and its antlers display Y-branched tines.

Very different from the graceful whitetail and blacktail is the moose, largest and most powerful of the deer. This strikingly homely creature has large ears, a bulbous nose, a pendulous upper lip, an absurdly protruding muzzle, and an inelegant clump of skin and hair—called a bell—dangling from the throat. Its short, hunchbacked body, set on disproportionately long front legs, is covered with long, coarse, black-brown hair. Adding to the generally awkward appearance are the antlers, enormous and flattened and bearing many points. The average bull moose stands almost 6 feet high at the shoulders and weighs between 1000 and 1400 pounds. In the United States

Black bear

moose may be found in the North from the Rockies to Maine.

Among the wild dogs of the woods are the red wolf and the gray wolf, and the red fox and the gray fox.

The red wolf is considerably smaller than its gray cousin, standing about 24 to 30 inches at the shoulder and weighing between 50 and 80 pounds. It has a black phase as well as the tawny red phase for which it was named.

The good-looking red fox has big black ears sitting erect atop a pointed head. Its golden-red body is borne on black legs, and its long bushy tail is clearly tipped with white. This fox weighs between 6 and 15 pounds, and stands 15 or 16 inches at the shoulder.

Approximately the same size is the gray fox, also called the tree fox because of its climbing talents. It wears a pepper-and-salt coat handsomely marked with orange, black, and white.

Although you will find American black bears in many North American forests, they are not necessarily black. They may, instead, be brown, cinnamon-colored, or even (in British Columbia) creamy white. The typical black bear has a brownish muzzle and a long, thick coat splashed with white on the chest. It stands between 2 and 3 feet at the shoulder, and weighs between 200 and 500 pounds, but its girth does not prevent it from climbing trees.

The raccoon is easily identified by the black mask it wears across the eyes and the black-and-buff alternating rings that decorate its 10-inch tail. The long, thick fur, brown-gray, yellowish, or blackish, gives the raccoon a sturdy appearance, but its average weight is only 15 pounds. You may encounter this creature beside a forest stream, fastidiously soaking a piece of meat in the water before eating it. Because of this unusual habit, the raccoon has been nicknamed "the washer."

The ferocious, flesh-eating weasel family has many members, and we will find most of them in our forests. Let's look for the marten and the fisher, the long-tailed weasel and the ermine, the mink, the wolverine, and the skunk.

The true marten is found in the treetops of thick forests, sunbathing on the limb of a large tree. Its cat-sized body, ending in a bushy tail, displays a soft, deep, beautiful fur of rich golden brown.

The fisher is a large dark-furred marten that weighs as much as 18 pounds and may measure as much as 4 feet, tail included. An agile climber, fleet runner, and strong swimmer, this fearless and powerful carnivore of the northern woods hunts all but the biggest beasts, even dining on porcupine.

Most familiar of the weasels is the long-tailed, whose ½-foot tail is only relatively long. The fur of this 6-ouncer is a deep red-brown to blackish, but in the animal's northern range the fur turns white in winter.

The ermine also wears white in wintertime, switching from its summer suit of yellow or chocolate-brown. In all seasons, however, its tail is tipped with black.

The mink very much resembles an overgrown weasel, with its long body and short limbs. Its highly sought-after fur is a lustrous dark-brown, sometimes spotted with white on the chin and throat.

Largest member of the weasel family, the wolverine has the build of a badger and the savagery of a wolf. It is, generally, a loner as it prowls the Northlands, destroying property, attacking almost any animal no matter the size, and leaving behind a foul-smelling odor of musk. This brown-furred beast measures between 36 and 44 inches and weighs between 20 and 50 pounds. Yellow bands appear on the sides and across the rump.

You will certainly need no warning to avoid displeasing a skunk. Peaceful as this mammal is, it will not hesitate, when threatened, to raise its tail and discharge an evil-smelling liquid from a pair of nozzles inside its anal tract. Two skunks to inspect—from a respectful distance—are the striped and the spotted.

The striped skunk wears a glossy black, long-haired coat with a bushy 7-inch tail at the end of its 18-inch head and body. The stripes for which it was named are white and broad, extending along each side from the tip of the tail and meeting on the head. Another white stripe appears between the eyes.

Smaller than the 4-to-10-pound striped skunk is the spotted skunk, which weighs only 1 or 2 pounds and is several inches shorter from end to end. This oddly marked animal has a great deal of white on its body, divided into an irregular pattern of lines and spots.

The cats of our forests include the cougar, which we have already met in the mountains, and the bob-

Raccoon

cat, whose paler brothers we have seen blending with the desert sand. Another forest cat is the Canadian lynx, found not only in Canada but in the northern forests of the United States.

Equipped with padded, oversized feet and powerful legs, the lynx is well prepared for moving easily through its snowy environment. It weighs 15 to 40 pounds, stands 22 to 24 inches at the shoulder, and wears a grizzled or gray-brown coat of long, soft fur. The lynx has a particularly attractive face, framed at the sides with a black-barred ruff, and its head is topped with heavily tufted ears. Strangely enough, this cat seems to like water and has been seen swimming with considerable skill.

Striped skunk

There are rodents aplenty in the forests of North America. The three main rodent groups include beavers and squirrels, rats and mice, and porcupines.

That well-constructed dam you see staying the forest waters was built by beavers, those admirable woodchoppers and architects. After felling trees with their powerful chisel teeth, the beavers dine on the inner bark and then use the rest of the wood for dams and lodges.

The beaver is also admired for its thick and hand-

Beaver

some dark-brown fur, and for its extraordinary abilities as a swimmer. This amphibious rodent can travel underwater for five to ten minutes without coming up for air. Webbed hind feet propel the sizeable body (30 to 70 pounds, 36 to 48 inches) through the water at two miles an hour, with the flat, scaly tail serving only as rudder.

Among the squirrels are tree squirrels, ground squirrels, and flying squirrels.

The red squirrel, a tree climber that lives in the evergreen forests of the North, is olive-gray with white underparts and a broad rusty band down its back. It is only 11 to 14 inches long and weighs about half a pound, but it is, nevertheless, famous for its noisy scolding tongue, which does not hesitate to tell off man or beast.

Western cousin of this red rodent is the Douglas squirrel, olive above and orange below and flaunting a yellow-fringed tail. Other tree squirrels include the pepper-and-salt-colored eastern gray squirrel, 16 to 21 inches long, and its slightly larger, more handsomely tailed cousin, the western gray squirrel; the big, good-looking Abert's squirrel, wearing ear tassels of tall black hairs; and the orange or brown-grizzled fox squirrel (largest in North America at 19 to 28 inches) named for its foxlike face.

We have already met some of the ground squirrels—the marmot of the mountains and the prairie dog of the plains. Let us look now at the snoopy, sociable chipmunks of the forest, one in the East and one in the West.

The 9-or 10-inch-long eastern chipmunk is distinguished by rusty-red hips and back, with black side stripes ending before the hip. Its head is pointed and two white stripes appear on each side of the face, one on the cheek and one above the eye. In the West the chipmunk is slimmer and wears five black and four white stripes to the base of the tail. Both chipmunks transport food in their cheek pouches, storing it in underground dwellings for nourishment during the winter months.

The woodchuck or groundhog is a ground squirrel, common in eastern United States, sometimes found at the forest edge. Its stocky 4-to-10-pound body, covered with grizzled fur, measures 18 to 26 inches in length.

If you are strolling through the forests at night you may see a long-furred, buff-colored creature gliding through the air. This is neither bird nor bat but the flying squirrel. Not actually able to fly, this squirrel can glide for 80 yards or more after leaping from a high perch, thanks to a thin membrane that extends on each side of the body from front to back limb. Look for the North American flying squirrel, found throughout the forested part of the continent. Its fur is fine and soft, its eyes dark and large, and its tail—which serves to control its gliding speed—is flattened and feathery.

Three mice to look for are the white-footed

mouse, the red tree mouse, and the red-backed mouse.

The white-footed mouse is a nocturnal creature spread throughout North America. Handsomely dressed in a fawn-colored coat and gleaming white vest, it has round black eyes, big ears, long whiskers, and a hairy tail.

The red tree mouse lives in the forests of the Pacific Coast, dining on the needles and bark of the young Douglas firs. These rodents have red coats and long black tails, weigh 1 to 1½ ounces, and measure 6¼ to 7 inches in length.

Slightly smaller is the pretty red-backed mouse, an active, industrious creature with a heavy appetite. Its furry body is splashed with red-brown along the back, and its sides are a lighter color.

Prickliest of the rodents is the porcupine, armored with some 30,000 quills averaging 1½ inches in length.

Woodchuck

Its chunky 15-pound body ends in a short, broad tail, and its limbs are tipped with strong, curved claws. You may come across the North American tree porcupine in the forests of North, East, and West. The eastern species has black hairs with a white band on the quills, while the western species has greenish-yellow hairs on its head. Porcupines are good-natured creatures that do not like to fight, but when necessary, their quills can serve as a painful and sometimes deadly weapon.

Rabbits are not rodents, although the two groups share a significant common trait—chisel-like front

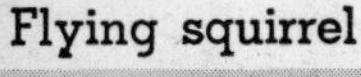

Flying squirrel

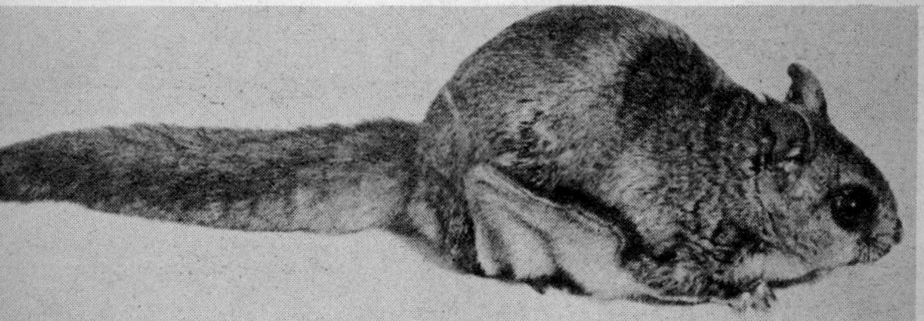

teeth. We have looked at pikas, rabbits, and hares on our various walks, so let us pause just briefly to examine the New England cottontail, found primarily in the open forests. The head and body of this rabbit measure 17 inches. Its fur is reddish in summer; in winter, it is sprinkled with white, giving it a reddish-gray appearance. There is a dark patch between the ears.

Very different from the fast-moving rabbit is the indolent opossum, America's only pouched mammal. This furry, gray-white marsupial weighs about 8 pounds and is approximately the size of a house cat. It has short legs, a bare, 10-inch prehensile tail that serves as an extra hand, and a white pointed face from which shine big, glossy eyes. Those who know opossums describe them as homely, ill-tempered, and stupid. When confronted with danger, they "play possum"—fall into a deceptive deathlike coma.

The cylindrical-shaped mole is a powerful digger, thanks to its broad forelegs tipped with sturdy claws. On the Pacific Coast you will find the Townsend mole, big and handsomely dressed in a black fur coat. It is 7 to 9 inches long and weighs 4 to 6 ounces. The star-nosed mole of the Northeast is also black, but you will have no difficulty distinguishing it from its western cousin. Just look for the striking decoration on its snout—twenty-two rose-colored tentacles!

The shrew family includes the tiniest mammals in the world, all with long, pointed heads, pinprick eyes, and short, rounded ears. Among the shrews are the common shrew, whose slim, brown-gray body measures 3 to 4½ inches; the long-tailed shrew, also called the red-toothed because of the brown-red pigment coating the tips of its teeth; and the short-tailed shrew, equipped with venomous saliva capable of killing a mouse.

Nature's only winged mammal, the bat, lives in a community, roosting by day and going abroad at night. There are three varieties that you may find in the forests.

The little brown bat, a dainty, dark-brown, round-eared creature, is common in North America. Its wingspan is about 10 inches.

The male red bat, most familiar of the tree bats, is distinctively clad in orange-red fur frosted with white. Ranging from Canada to Panama, except for the Rockies, this sturdy mammal travels on narrow, tapered wings with a 12-inch spread.

The pallid bat, biggest of the three, has large ears and relatively slow-moving wings that spread about 14 inches. Look for this mammal in the forests of the West Coast.

Like mammals everywhere, the forest mammals we have just seen are well adapted to their environment. The difficulties of the cold winter months,

Porcupine

Opossum

when the threat to survival is greatest, are dealt with in a number of effective ways. Some animals, like the deer, continue to move about even in the harshest weather, protected by their warm winter coats. Many others, the bear and the chipmunk, for instance, retreat into sleep—a torpor or deep hibernation. Skunks and foxes prepare for winter hardship by fattening themselves throughout the summer and fall. During the same period beavers providently gather and store food. And so, although the forest is at its most difficult when the snows descend, life goes steadily on, ready to burst into activity when the first buds of spring appear.

Forest Reptiles

We have looked at lizards and snakes in many parts of the country—the high mountains, the semiarid plains, and the dry deserts. Before we go on to forest reptiles, let us see what general observations can be made about these two members of the order Squamata.

Lizards, represented by nearly 3000 species, live all over the world in many different environments. Most are terrestrial, but some climb trees, others are subterranean, several are semimarine, and there are even a few that glide through the air.

The lizard's skin is dry, with scales that range from small granules to prominent spines. Periodically this skin is shed. Most lizards have well-developed clawed limbs with five toes on each of the four feet. The tail in many cases is fragile and easily broken, but when lost it can readily be replaced.

Lizards see very well and have an acute sense of smell, but they do not seem to notice sound. Almost none of them has a voice.

The adhesive saliva on the lizard's tongue serves as an efficient food trap. Out flicks the tongue and an insect, centipede, or other tiny creature is caught on the surface and drawn into the mouth.

Snakes, like lizards, are represented by almost

3000 species and are adapted to a broad variety of environments. Distribution is nearly worldwide. Snakes may be found on the ground, under the ground, in salt and fresh water, and up a tree.

Scales are arranged down the body in longitudinal rows. They are usually overlapping, but size and shape vary greatly from species to species. All snakes are limbless, though in some families vestiges remain. Like lizards, snakes replace their skins periodically, but they cannot, as their relatives do, regenerate a missing tail.

Eyesight is good and so is the sense of smell. But snakes probably cannot hear air-borne vibrations, including the rattler's rattle. Almost all snakes hiss by expelling air from the lungs.

Snakes dine on all sorts of animals and birds' eggs, overpowering their live prey by seizing, squeezing, or introducing venom. They are capable of swallowing objects dramatically larger than themselves.

Lizards and snakes are cold-blooded, depending on outside sources of heat to keep their bodies warm. Thus they are most abundant in tropical regions, avoiding deep forests where the tight-locked canopy of treetops shuts out the sun. Several can be found, however, on forest fringes and in the open woods.

You can see ground, five-lined, and broad-headed skinks (smooth, shiny lizards) in the eastern half of North America, while western and Gilbert skinks are found in the West.

The dainty ground skink, 3 to 4¾ inches long, comes in a variety of brown shades—red, golden, chocolate, blackish—with a dorsolateral dark stripe and a white or yellow belly. The five-lined skink, a basically terrestrial creature that sometimes climbs trees to seek insects, is distinctively marked in its youth with a vivid blue tail, black ground color, and five white or yellow stripes. In adults (5 to 7½ inches long) the tail turns gray and the pattern fades, but you can still detect light stripes in the female and traces of them in the male. The females and young of the broad-headed skink are patterned like the five-lined, but the big male, which sometimes measures 12⅜ inches, is olive-brown with a red head and puffy jowls.

Well-defined dark stripes and, sometimes, light stripes mark the western skink, which also displays red touches and a bluish belly. The snout-vent length is 2½ to 3¼ inches, with the tail 1½ times this head-body measurement. The Gilbert skink may be close to 11 inches long, with a red head, pinkish-red tail, and a pale-bellied body that is olive-brown above and blue-green on the sides.

Spiny lizards (those with keeled and pointed dorsal scales) include the eastern and western fence lizard, Clark's spiny lizard, and the sagebrush lizard.

The 4-to-7¼-inch eastern fence lizard is gray or brown. Females have a conspicuous pattern of dark, wavy crosslines on top, while males are distinctively marked with blue bordered with black on the sides and throat. The western fence lizard, which we met on our mountain walk, is one of the most common and best known in the Sierras.

The grayish or greenish Clark's spiny lizard wears black crossbands on forearms and wrists and measures 3 to 5 inches in snout-vent length. The sagebrush lizard, 4½ to 5 inches long, is greenish or brownish-gray above, white below, with rust behind the forelegs or on the sides and pale blue at the throat and on the sides of the belly. You will find this lizard not only in the sagebrush but around chaparral thickets.

Alligator lizards, like the one we saw in the mountains, are also western forest dwellers. Look for the foothill alligator lizard, with a light-brown, olive-gray, or dull-yellow ground color and irregular dark bands marking the body and tail. Adults are 4 to 6½ inches in snout-vent length, with a tail more than double this head-body measurement.

The northern brown snake, 9 to 13 inches long, frequents moist woods from Maine to Virginia. Its belly is pale and its brown back has blackish spots set in two parallel rows. A dark streak appears at the side of the head.

Woods are one of many habitats for that common reptile, the eastern garter snake, an 18-to-26-incher. Its basic color may be black, brown, green, or olive, and typically three yellowish stripes, separated by rows of black spots, can be seen. Black spots also appear, indistinctly, on the greenish or yellowish belly.

Ring-necked snakes live in the woods of East and West. The 10-to-15-inch northern ringneck is dark and slim, with a yellow belly and a collar of gold. The 12-to-22-inch western ringneck is olive, blue-gray, or blackish above and yellow-orange, orange, or coral below, with a red, yellow, or orange neck band and black dots on its belly.

Worm snakes and racers may be found in the woods. There is the western worm snake, purple-black above and pink below, with a pointed head at one end of its 7½-to-11-inch length. There is the slender blue racer, 36 to 60 inches and dull blue all over. And there is the eastern yellow-bellied racer, 30 to 50 inches, which may be brown, gray, olive, or blue with a yellowish belly.

In the eastern half of the country various pine snakes—large, powerful, and constricting—frequent the woods for which they are named. The northern pine snake, 48 to 66 inches long, has a light ground color marked with conspicuous dark blotches. The 48-to-56-inch Louisiana pine snake is also light with dark blotches, the ones near the head running together, the ones near the tail clearly separated. The western relatives of the pine snakes are called gopher snakes. They may also be found in the woods.

Among the wood-dwelling kingsnakes and milk snakes of East and West are the eastern kingsnake, the California mountain kingsnake, and the Coastal Plain milk snake.

The eastern kingsnake has an unmistakable pattern of white or cream-colored links standing out against a shiny, dark background. It measures 36 to 48 inches long.

At 21 to 30 inches, the California mountain kingsnake is considerably smaller than its eastern relative. This handsome serpent displays a pattern of alternating black and white rings with occasional touches of red.

The Coastal Plain milk snake, 21 to 35 inches long, is basically gray, tan, or yellow, this ground color dominated by big reddish blotches bordered in black. A conspicuous collar appears at the neck and the whitish belly is clearly spotted with black.

Dangerously poisonous snakes live in the woods of East and West.

The eastern coral snake, sometimes found among the pines, is 20 to 30 inches long. Bright red and yellow rings encircle the body, a broad yellow band marks the head, and the end of the snout is black.

The northern copperhead is named for the reddish-copper of its head. Hourglass markings, dark-chestnut in color, decorate its 24-to-36-inch body. Although frequently referred to as a "moccasin," this snake should be called by its proper name.

Dark blotches and light spots mark the eastern massasauga, a 20-to-30-inch rattler. The ground color is gray and the belly is black with light markings.

The timber rattlesnake, which we have met in the mountains, is also a woodland resident. So is the ridge-nosed rattlesnake, 18 to 24 inches long, a Westerner blotched, spotted, and striped in brown, black, white, and gray.

Forest Insects and Other Arthropods

In our nature walks we have met representatives of the six principal classes of the phylum Arthropoda. We found two groups, the horseshoe crabs and the crustaceans, dwelling beside the sea. The other four groups—insects, spiders and their relatives, millipedes, and centipedes—can be found in the forest.

Like all arthropods, insects have jointed appendages and segmented bodies covered with a limy or horny shell. But while the other classes have two main body divisions, insects have three—head, thorax (chest), and abdomen. Insects are also characterized by a maximum of three pairs of legs, one pair of antennae and, as a rule, one or two pairs of wings.

In developing from the egg to the adult, most insects undergo a series of changes called metamorphosis. In a few insects, however, the newly hatched form shows no difference from the adult except in size and absence of sexual activity. This type of insect has no metamorphosis. When the basic difference between the newly hatched insect and the adult is merely the development of functional wings, we say metamorphosis is incomplete, and the young insect is generally called a nymph. In complete metamorphosis, the wormlike newly hatched insect is called a larva and behaves differently from the full-grown insect, passing into an inactive intermediate stage—the pupa—before achieving adulthood.

There are more species of the class Insecta than of all other plants and animals combined. Some 900,000 have been classified so far, and scientists predict that the total number of species will eventually add up to at least 2,000,000. According to some expert classifications, there are twenty-four insect orders. Each order has up to several hundred families, each family may have hundreds of genera, and each genus has many individual species. Instead of looking for individual species, then, let us examine the general characteristics of some important insect orders and families, all of which have forest representatives.

Springtails (order Collembola) are primitive wingless insects that can jump into the air thanks to a springlike mechanism on the underside of the abdomen. These tiny creatures, usually under 1/16 of an inch long, are generally pale, but some may be dark-gray, blue, or red. Look for them in the forest under damp leaves or logs.

Most primitive of the winged insects is the order Orthoptera, which includes roaches, mantids, walking-

Praying mantis

sticks, locusts, grasshoppers and crickets, and the grylloblattas seen on a mountain walk. Some are wingless, but the majority have two pairs of wings, the leathery front ones narrower, thicker, and stronger than the membranous rear ones, often with a camouflage coloring of greens and browns. The larger rear wings, which may be orange, red, and yellow, are folded in fanwise pleats when not in use. Sizes vary from crickets under ½ inch long to walkingsticks as long as 1 foot. Many of these insects are music-makers, a strictly masculine accomplishment produced by rubbing the legs or wings together.

The flat-bodied cockroach, no larger than slightly over 2 inches in our country, has long, slender legs well adapted for running. City dwellers may know this insect only as a household pest, but many roaches can be found out of doors, under dead bark, and in decaying vegetation. Many are brown but some may be green or yellow to match the plants among which they sometimes live.

The mantid is familiarly called the praying mantis, because its front pincher legs, adapted for capturing other insects, are held in a praying position. Many of the voracious predatory mantids are green, often with a leaflike pattern on the front wings. Others simulate bark, with colors of gray and brown. Sizes range from 4 or 5 inches to under an inch.

If a twig gets up and starts to walk away, don't be alarmed. It isn't a hallucination but a walking-stick—elongated, wingless, and totally twiglike in appearance. These unusual insects are plant eaters that dine on the foliage of trees.

While several grasshoppers live on the Great Plains, a few grasshopper and locust species live in the forest too. A well-known longhorn grasshopper is the katydid, a narrow-bodied, bright-green insect with broad wings which make a rasping noise when rubbed together.

Crickets may be found in trees, on the ground, or buried under the soil. The most common cricket in this country is the field cricket, which is black and about 1 inch long.

Termites, sometimes miscalled "white ants," are wood eaters that belong to the order Isoptera. Their two pairs of membranous wings are almost equal in size and their bodies are soft. They bear a superficial resemblance to ants, and like them are social insects. Termite society is composed of several castes, including winged sexual males and females (from which come the wingless kings and queens) and sterile workers and soldiers.

Order Heteroptera is composed of the true bugs, slow-moving insects with long, slim legs, smooth bodies (occasionally hairy or spiny), and jointed beaks that rise from the front of the head. Rear wings are completely membranous, while forewings are membranous only at the outer ends and are thick and leathery on the basal half (or two-thirds of the wing). Among the many true bugs are the 1/4-to-1/2-inch stink bugs, dominant members of the order, usually brown but sometimes green, brightly variegated, or metallic; the red, white, and black chinch bugs; the minute lace bugs, found on many broad-leaved trees; water striders and water boatmen and other aquatic bugs.

The cicadas and their relatives belong to the order Homoptera, distinguished from the true bugs in two important ways: The beak is attached beneath and

Cicada

to the rear of the head, and both pairs of wings are uniformly membranous. Because the mouth parts of the two orders are the same, they are sometimes grouped together and called the Hemiptera.

The male cicada is considered the noisiest insect in the world. Cicadas are large and robust, with broad heads and protruding eyes. Their relatives include planthoppers, treehoppers, leafhoppers, aphids, and scale insects.

We have seen damselflies and dragonflies on our mountain walk. These lovely members of the order Odonata may also be found near forest waterways.

Any insect beauty contest is likely to be dominated by members of the order Lepidoptera—the moths and butterflies. The large wings of almost all these flying flowers are covered with tiny overlapping scales that provide exquisite colors and intricate patterns. Elaborate colors and designs are also present in the larval stage, when moths and butterflies are humble caterpillars.

Butterflies and moths range in size from those

with $\frac{1}{8}$-inch wingspans to giants that spread their wings 11 or 12 inches. Although not as important as the bees, they are valuable in the cross-pollination of our flowering plants.

There are exceptions to almost every rule given to distinguish moths from butterflies, so we won't bother to repeat them here. Let us look at just a few examples from this second largest of the insect orders.

The hawk or sphinx moths are a well-known family, with heavy, torpedo-shaped bodies, long pointed forewings, and small hind wings. Many are beautifully colored and patterned, with bright rear wings and front wings mottled or streaked in tans, browns, or grays.

A major forest pest is the family of tortricid moths, which dine on both coniferous and deciduous trees. Tortricids usually have a maximum wingspread of 1 inch and display attractive stripes or spots in browns or grays. The resting adults have a bell-like shape when viewed from above.

Standing between the moths and butterflies are

Swallowtail

Monarch butterfly

the skippers, which exhibit some characteristics of both groups. Skippers are day fliers with stout, hairy bodies, the majority plainly colored in yellows and browns.

Physically largest of our butterflies are the swallowtails; numerically largest are the nymphalids. Most swallowtails are brightly colored, many with two or three tail-like extensions on each hind wing. The head is rather large and the wings are strong. The nymphalid butterflies have reduced forelegs and the antennae are knobbed more than is usual.

Blues, coppers, and hairstreaks form a family of small butterflies with a wingspread of ¾ to 1½ inches. These are bright-colored insects, sometimes in iridescent blues or greens or coppery tones, with eyes distinctively bordered with white scales.

One of the most interesting butterfly families, the milkweed butterflies, includes the outstanding monarch. This is a migratory insect that moves south in cool weather, heading northward when the spring arrives. Unlike birds, monarchs fly during the warm hours of the day. At night thousands of them cluster together on the trees, displaying their orange wings dramatically bordered with black and spotted with white.

Most numerous of the insects are the beetles, sole members of the order Coleoptera. In most beetles the first pair of wings, hard and veinless, are curved in shield fashion over the abdomen and over the second pair of wings, which are large, thin, and membranous. Otherwise beetles show great variation in all features, including size, which ranges from 1/100 inch to 6 inches.

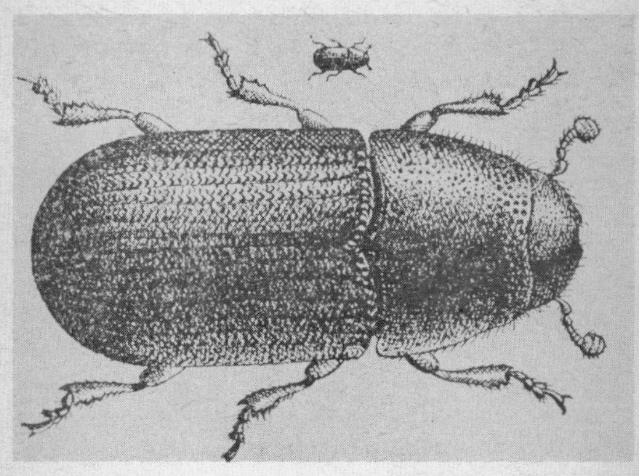

Western pine beetle

The familiar ladybugs or ladybirds are a family of beetles. Many are bright red, orange, or pink with spots of black; others reverse the color pattern. Rarely are they longer than ¼ inch.

Another familiar beetle is the firefly, which bears the nickname lightningbug because of its luminous greenish-yellow light. Fireflies are flat and elongated with soft black or brown forewings.

The handsome tiger beetle, whose larva is called the doodlebug, is present almost all over the world. It is ½ to 1 inch long, with long, thin legs, bulging eyes, and sharp jaws. Most species are dull brown or black, but some are iridescent blue, green, purple, orange, or scarlet. In the woodlands look for the six-spotted tiger beetle, brilliant green or blue with white dots on the forewings.

Ground beetles can be found in open woods. They are flatter, broader, and heavier-bodied than tiger beetles, with shorter legs and less bulging eyes. Most are black or brown, but a few are iridescent, metallic, or brightly colored. Often the hind wings are absent.

The true flies belong to the order Diptera, the fourth largest order of insects. The members of this order differ from such insects as butterflies, dragonflies, fireflies, and so forth, by having one pair of wings. Instead of hind wings the fly displays "halteres," tiny knobs mounted on short stalks which serve as balancers. Another outstanding characteristic of the true fly is its very large eyes, which sometimes occupy most of the head. Among the Diptera are crane flies, mosquitoes, midges, buffalo gnats, robber flies, and fruit flies. An outstanding pest of the North Woods is the black fly—stout, humpbacked, and short-legged.

Except for termites, all the social insects belong to the order Hymenoptera, third largest of the insect orders. These include the wasps, the ants, and the bees. Members of this order have two pairs of wings—veined, transparent, membranous—with a row of tiny hooks fastening the hind wings to the wings up front.

Velvet ants are really brightly colored wasps covered with dense, usually short hairs. The wingless females are red or yellow, banded and patterned with white, black, or brown. The winged males are black, with markings of red or orange on the abdomen.

The large Vespidae family includes both social

Wasp

and solitary wasps. The social group is composed of hornets, yellow jackets, and other so-called paper wasps—those that construct nests of coarse paper made from wood fiber. The solitary group includes the potter wasps, which use clay to build nests that may take the form of perfect jugs and vases. These insects are often brightly marked with white, yellow, or red.

All ants belong to the Formicidae family. Naked or hairy, black, brown, reddish, or yellow, these gregarious creatures always live in colonies composed of fertile females (queens), males (which die shortly after mating), and infertile females (workers, soldiers, and other castes). Our largest ant is the black carpenter ant, a common species found throughout the eastern half of the United States. The common red ant of the genus *Formica* may be found in open woods under tall trees.

The bees comprise several families, but the largest is the Apidae, which includes the carpenter bee

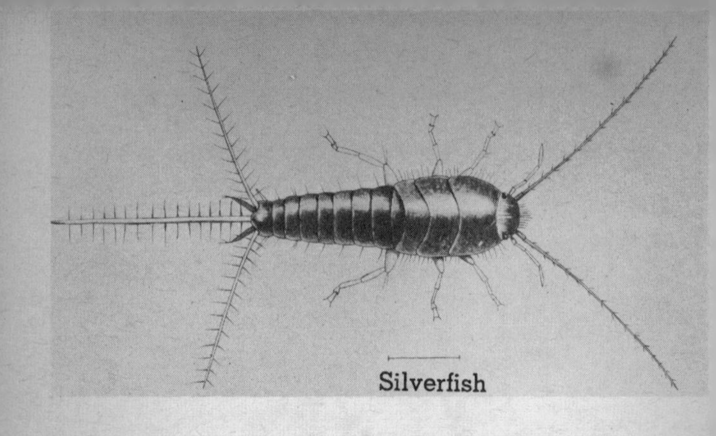

Silverfish

and our well-known bumblebees and honeybees. Some are social, some solitary, some parasitic.

Bumblebees are covered with dense hair and have black coats marked with yellow, orange, or red. The honeybee is dark to golden in color. Both groups live in colonies of queens (fertile females), workers (infertile females), and drones (stingless sexual males).

We have no time to look at the other insect orders, but if you are interested in investigating them, here are their names.

The very primitive groups include, in addition to the springtails, the silvery bristletails or silverfish of order Thysanura and the minute proturans of order Protura. Several small orders, sharing in common an incomplete metamorphosis, are the earwigs (order Dermaptera), the thrips (order Thysanoptera), the embiids (order Embioptera), and the booklice and their relatives (order Psocoptera). Two aquatic groups not discussed here are the mayflies (order Ephemeroptera) and the stoneflies (order Plecoptera). Parasites include sucking lice (order Anoplura), biting lice (order Mallophaga), fleas (order Siphonaptera). Three small groups are the scorpion flies (order Mecoptera); lacewings, ant lions, dobson flies, etc., (order Neuroptera); and the caddisflies (order Trichoptera).

The class Arachnida—with many representatives in the forest—includes not only spiders, but daddy longlegs, scorpions, ticks, mites, and chiggers. In contrast with the insects, this group of arthropods has a two-part body division (cephalothorax and abdomen), four pairs of legs, and no antennae or wings.

Most spiders have fangs and poison glands, and all can produce silk thread. But not every spider spins a web. Commonly gray or brown, spiders may sometimes be as brilliantly colored as butterflies. About 30,000 species have been described, of which 2000 or more are found in the United States. Look for them among the moss and dead leaves of the woods.

The daddy longlegs is sometimes, but not always, considered a spider. It does, indeed, have long legs, the two front pairs being particularly long and slender. The most common species, all of the genus *Leiobunum,* are small-bodied creatures with a yellow to dark-brown color.

Forests are not the normal habitat of scorpions and the stingerless whip scorpions, which we have seen in the desert. But the up-to-¼-inch pseudoscorpion, which looks like a scorpion in miniature, may be found there.

Mites, ticks, and chiggers are usually no bigger than ½ inch and many of the group are microscopic. Bodies are generally spherical and shaped like an egg, with several North American species displaying a red color. Those that are not parasitic feed on tiny plants and animals and on the decaying matter found on the forest floor.

Millipedes, sole members of the class Diplopoda, have two major body divisions (head and body), one pair of short antennae, and two pairs of legs per segment—never adding up to as many as 1000. They are vegetarian land dwellers with no poison glands.

Centipedes, sole members of the class Chilopoda, also have two major body divisions (head and body) and one pair of antennae, which are long. They have one pair of legs per segment, sometimes totalling considerably more than 100. These land dwellers are flesh eaters, and wear a pair of poison fangs on the first body segment.

Birds of the Forest

No animals other than birds possess feathers. Body feathers insulate, while wing and tail feathers aid in flight. Almost all birds fly, but there are a few nonfliers that belong to the class Aves.

Birds are toothless, warm-blooded creatures with distinctive and varied songs and nest-building habits. They have better vision, both long-distance and close, than any other animal, excellent hearing, and a poor sense of smell. Some feed on seeds and some on insects, while other food preferences include mice, fish, or frogs. Little is yet understood about their marvelous ability to navigate, an ability that enables them to find their way on annual round-trip migrations that sometimes encompass 22,000 miles.

Some 8600 different bird species exist throughout the world, with 796 found in North America. With so many birds to see, we have chosen to emphasize land birds. We will look now at some of the most familiar and common land birds of the woods.

Everyone knows the 9-to-11-inch robin, a bird of both eastern and western woods. It has a yellow bill, a gray back, and a readily recognized brick-red breast. (The breasts of young robins are speckled.)

An eastern member of the same family is the wood thrush; in the West it is the hermit thrush. The wood thrush has a rusty head and is heavily spotted on the breast and sides. The hermit thrush was seen on our mountain walk.

The crested flycatcher and the Acadian flycatcher are eastern birds. The eastern wood peewee is a sparrow-sized member of the same family.

The 8-to-9-inch crested flycatcher is unique among the flycatchers in having a rufous tail. It is large and yellow-bellied with a gray throat and gray breast.

Considerably smaller is the greenish Acadian flycatcher. It is marked by two white wing bars and a light eye ring.

The eastern wood peewee also has wing bars but no eye ring. It is olive-brown above and whitish below.

Look for the scarlet tanager in the East and its cross-country cousin, the western tanager. The male scarlet tanager is, indeed, the color of his name, with black wings and tail. The male western tanager, distinguished by wing bars from other tanagers, is yellow, red-faced, and black-winged.

In the deciduous forests of the East, look for these warblers—cerulean, hooded, and Kentucky.

The male cerulean warbler is blue above and white below, with a narrow black ring on the upper breast. The female, also whitish below, is blue-gray and olive-green above and has two white wing bars and a white line over the eyes.

The hooded warbler is named for the appearance of the male, who wears a black hood around his yel-

Wood thrush

Lake
Nº 2 HUNTING
AREA
(WEST)

Mattamuskeet National Wildlife Refuge

low face and forehead. The female is olive above and has a vivid yellow coloring on forehead and underparts.

Black "sideburns" and yellow "spectacles" distinguish both male and female Kentucky warblers.

Other common forest members of the warbler family are the Louisiana water thrush; the oven bird, found in both East and West; and Audubon's warbler, a western bird we have seen in the mountains.

The Louisiana water thrush is a gray bird with a pure white eye stripe. Underparts are light-colored and heavily striped. The oven bird is a sparrow-sized warbler, olive-brown above and striped below. It has pale pink legs and a light orange patch on the top of its head.

The vireo family resembles the warblers, but its members have heavier bills and are less active. Look for the red-eyed vireo, olive-green above and white below, found in the East. A white stripe bordered with black appears over the eye, and it wears a gray cap on its head.

Another Easterner is the tufted titmouse. This is a small, gray mouse-colored bird with rusty flanks and a tufted crest.

Western forest representatives of the Fringillidae family include the black-headed grosbeak and the Oregon junco.

The male grosbeak is an outstanding bird with his rust-colored breast, black head, black-and-white wings, and pale bill. The female is brown and streaked.

The male Oregon junco comes in two varieties. He may have a brown back, rust or buff sides, and a black head. Or he may have pinkish sides, a dull brown back, and a gray hood.

Look also in the West for the golden crowned kinglet, the hairy woodpecker, and the brown creeper.

The golden crowned kinglet is olive-gray with a white stripe over the eye. Males wear an orange-red crown patch; females wear yellow.

The hairy woodpecker has a white beak and a large bill.

The brown creeper is a tree-climbing bird with a brown back. It climbs up a tree spirally, then flies to the next and starts at the bottom again.

Out of the Woods

The American forests we have seen were greater by a third only 300 years ago. In 1620, it is told, a squirrel could travel from the Atlantic Coast to the banks of the Mississippi without ever touching the ground.

Not only forests, but all the natural communities have suffered from man's thoughtlessness and his greed. And not only trees but many forms of wildlife have been depleted or completely extinguished.

The survival of our wild and beautiful regions and the creatures that live within them depends on laws that offer protection both to habitat and inhabitants. And these laws depend, eventually, on you—on your love and understanding of the natural world and your willingness to work for its conservation.

APPENDIX

The Plant Kingdom

Phylum Thallophyta—algae, fungi, lichens
Phylum Bryophyta—liverworts and mosses
Phylum Tracheophyta—vascular plants
Subphylum Psilopsida—most primitive vascular plants
Subphylum Lycopsida—includes *Lepidodendron* and *Sigillaria*
Subphylum Sphenopsida—includes *Calamites* and scouring rushes
Subphylum Pteropsida
  Class Filicineae—ferns
  Class Gymnospermae—plants with naked seeds
    Order Gnetales—close resemblance to angiosperms
    Order Coniferales—conifers
    Order Ginkgoales—ginkgoes
    Order Cordaitales—*Cordaites*
    Order Cycadales—living cycads
    Order Cycadeoidales—extinct cycadlike plants
    Order Cycadofilicales—primitive gymnosperms
  Class Angiospermae—flowering plants
    Subclass Monocotyledonae—seed with single cotyledon
    Subclass Dicotyledonae—seed with two cotyledons

The Animal Kingdom

Phylum Protozoa—unicellular animals
Phylum Porifera—sponges
Phylum Coelenterata
  Class Hydrozoa—hydroids
  Class Scyphozoa—jellyfish
  Class Anthozoa—corals and sea anemones
Phylum Ctenophora—comb jellies
Phylum Platyhelminthes—flatworms
Phylum Nemertea—ribbon worms

Phylum Nematoda[1]—roundworms
Phylum Rotatoria[2]—rotifers
Phylum Nematomorpha[3]—horsehair worms
Phylum Bryozoa—moss animals
Phylum Brachiopoda—lamp shells
Phylum Echinodermata
- Class Asteroidea—starfish
- Class Opiuroidea—brittle and basket stars
- Class Echinoidea—sea urchins and sand dollars
- Class Holothuroidea—sea cucumbers
- Class Crinoidea—sea lilies

Phylum Mollusca
- Class Pelecypoda—clams, mussels, etc.
- Class Amphineura—chitons
- Class Gastropoda—snails, etc.
- Class Scaphopoda—tooth shells
- Class Cephalopoda—squids, etc.

Phylum Annelida—segmented worms
Phylum Onychophora[4]
Phylum Arthropoda
- Class Crustacea—shrimps, crabs, barnacles
- Class Paleostracha—horseshoe crabs
- Class Diplopoda—millipedes
- Class Chilopoda—centipedes
- Class Insecta—bees, grasshoppers, beetles, etc.
- Class Arachnida—spiders, ticks, etc.

Phylum Chordata
- Subphylum Hemichorda—acorn worms
- Subphylum Urochorda—tunicates
- Subphylum Cephalochorda—lancelet
- Subphylum Vertebrata—vertebrates
  - Class Agnatha—lampreys, hagfishes
  - Class Chondrichthyes—sharks, rays
  - Class Osteichthyes—bony fishes
  - Class Amphibia—salamanders, frogs, toads
  - Class Reptilia—turtles, snakes, lizards, alligators
  - Class Aves—birds
  - Class Mammalia—mammals

[1] This phylum was not discussed in the text. The Nematoda have an elongated, cylindrical body, usually pointed at both ends. Some are parasitic but many are free living.

[2] The Rotatoria (not discussed in the text) are microscopic fresh-water dwellers with circles of cilia at the sides of the mouth.

[3] The Nematomorpha (not discussed in the text) are long, thin worms.

[4] The Onychophora (not discussed in the text) are wormlike terrestrial animals, intermediate between Annelida and Arthropoda, which occur in moist tropics and subtropics.

General Bibliography

Barker, Will. *Familiar Animals of America.* Harper and Brothers, 1956.

Burt, William Henry. *A Field Guide to the Mammals.* Houghton Mifflin Company, 1952.

Collins, Henry Hill, Jr. *Complete Field Guide to American Wildlife.* Harper and Brothers, 1959.

Conant, Roger. *A Field Guide to Reptiles and Amphibians.* Houghton Mifflin Company, 1958.

Drimmer, Frederick (ed.). *The Animal Kingdom* (3 volumes), Greystone Press, 1954.

Hall, Eugene Raymond, and Keith R. Kelson. *Mammals of North America.* Ronald Press, 1959.

Hamilton, William J. *Mammals of Eastern United States.* Hafner Publishing Co., 1943.

Klots, Alexander B. *A Field Guide to the Butterflies.* Houghton Mifflin Company, 1951.

—— *Living Insects of the World.* Doubleday & Company, Inc., 1959.

Mathews, F. Schuyler. *Field Book of American Wildflowers.* G. P. Putnam's Sons, 1955.

National Geographic Society. *Wild Animals of North America.* National Geographic Society, 1960.

Oliver, J. A. *The Natural History of North American Amphibians and Reptiles.* D. Van Nostrand Co., 1955.

Peterson, Roger Tory. *A Field Guide to the Birds.* Houghton Mifflin Company, 1947.

—— *A Field Guide to Western Birds.* Houghton Mifflin Company, 1961.

Pettingill, O. Sewall, Jr. *A Guide to Bird Finding East of the Mississippi.* Oxford University Press, 1951.

—— *A Guide to Bird Finding West of the Mississippi.* Oxford University Press, 1953.

Pough, Richard H. *Audubon Land Bird Guide.* Doubleday & Company, Inc., 1949.

Schmidt, Karl P., and Robert F. Inger. *Living Reptiles of the World.* Hanover House, 1957.

Stebbins, Robert C. *Amphibians and Reptiles of Western North America.* McGraw-Hill Book Company, 1954.
Swain, Ralph B. *The Insect Guide.* Doubleday & Company, Inc., 1948.

PAST

American Geological Institute. *Geology and Earth Sciences Sourcebook.* Holt, Rinehart & Winston, Inc., 1962.
Ames, Gerald, and Rose Wyler. *The Earth's Story.* Creative Educational Society, Inc., 1957.
Andrews, Roy Chapman. *All About Strange Beasts of the Past.* Random House, Inc., 1956.
Barnett, Lincoln, and the Editorial Staff of *Life. The World We Live In,* Time, Inc., 1955.
Carrington, Richard. *A Guide to Earth History.* Mentor Books (The New American Library), 1956.
Darling, Lois and Louis. *Before and After Dinosaurs.* William Morrow & Co., Inc., 1959.
Gamow, George. *A Planet Called Earth.* Viking Press, 1963.
Kummel, Bernhard. *History of the Earth.* W. H. Freeman & Co., 1961.
Lauber, Patricia. *All About the Ice Age.* Random House, Inc., 1959.
Pearl, Richard M. *Geology.* Barnes & Noble, Inc., 1960.
Riedman, Sarah R. *Naming Living Things.* Rand McNally & Co., 1963.
Romer, Alfred S. *The Vertebrate Story.* University of Chicago Press, 1959.
Swinton, William Elgin. *The Wonderful World of Prehistoric Animals.* Garden City Books, 1961.

SEASHORE

Abbott, R. Tucker. *American Seashells.* D. Van Nostrand Co., Inc., 1954.
Arnold, Augusta Foote. *The Sea-Beach at Ebb-Tide.* The Century Co., 1916.
Bent, Arthur Cleveland. *Life Histories of North American Shore Birds,* Part I and Part II. Dover Publications, Inc., 1962.
Berrill, N. J. and Jacquelyn. *1001 Questions Answered About the Seashore.* Dodd, Mead & Co., 1957.
Buchsbaum, Ralph. *Animals Without Backbones.* University of California Press, 1948.

Buchsbaum, Ralph, and Lorus J. Milne. *The Lower Animals.* Doubleday & Company, Inc., 1960.
Carson, Rachel. *The Edge of the Sea.* Houghton Mifflin Company, 1955.
Cooper, Elizabeth K. *Science on the Shores and Banks.* Harcourt, Brace & Co., 1960.
Engel, Leonard, and the Editors of *Life. The Sea.* Time, Inc., 1961.
Hall, Henry Marion. *A Gathering of Shore Birds.* Devin-Adair Co., 1960.
MacGinitie, G. E. and N. *Natural History of Marine Animals.* McGraw-Hill Book Company, 1949.
Miner, Roy Waldo. *Field Book of Seashore Life.* G. P. Putnam's Sons, 1950.
Selsam, Millicent. *See Along the Shore.* Harper and Brothers, 1961.
Zim, Herbert S., and Lester Ingle. *Seashores.* Simon and Schuster, Inc., 1955.

MOUNTAIN

Craighead, John J., Frank C. Craighead, Jr., and Ray J. Davis. *A Field Guide to Rocky Mountain Wildflowers.* Houghton Mifflin Company, 1963.
Farb, Peter. *Face of North America* (Chapter IV, The Mountains). Harper & Row, 1963.
Fenton, Carroll Lane, and Mildred Adams Fenton. *Mountains.* Doubleday, Doran & Co., Inc., 1942.
Huxley, Anthony (ed.). *Standard Encyclopedia of the World's Mountains.* G. P. Putnam's Sons, 1962.
Lane, Dr. Ferdinand C. *The Story of Mountains.* Doubleday & Company, Inc., 1950.
Milne, Lorus J., and Margery Milne, and the Editors of *Life. The Mountains.* Time, Inc., 1962.
Peattie, Roderick (ed.). *The Berkshires.* Vanguard Press, 1948.
—— (ed.). *The Black Hills.* Vanguard Press, 1952.
—— (ed.). *The Friendly Mountains.* Vanguard Press, 1942.
—— (ed.). *The Great Smokies and the Blue Ridge.* Vanguard Press, 1943.
—— *Mountain Geography.* Harvard University Press, 1936.
—— *The Pacific Coast Ranges.* Vanguard Press, 1946.
Storer, Tracy I., and Robert L. Usinger. *Sierra Nevada Natural History.* University of California Press, 1963.

Stupka, Arthur. *Great Smoky Mountains National Park.* National Park Service, 1960.
Willard, Bettie E., and Chester O. Harris. *Alpine Wildflowers of Rocky Mountain National Park.* Rocky Mountain Nature Association, 1963.

GREAT PLAINS

Goetz, Delia. *Grasslands.* William Morrow & Co., Inc., 1959.
Kraenzel, Carl Frederick. *The Great Plains in Transition.* University of Oklahoma Press, 1955.
Pool, Raymond J. *Marching with the Grasses.* University of Nebraska Press, 1948.
Pounds, N. J. G. *North America* (Chapter 10, The Great Plains). John Murray, 1959.
Shaw, Earl B. *Anglo-America: A Regional Geography* (Chapter 11, The Great Plains). John Wiley & Sons, Inc., 1959.
United States Department of Agriculture. *Grasshoppers—A New Look at an Ancient Enemy* (Farmers' Bulletin No. 2064). U.S. Government Printing Office, 1957.
Weaver, J. E., and F. W. Albertson. *Grasslands of the Great Plains.* Johnsen Publishing Co., 1956.
Weaver, J. E. *North American Prairie.* Johnsen Publishing Co., 1954.
Werner, Jane, and the Staff of the Walt Disney Studio. *Vanishing Prairie.* Simon and Schuster, Inc., 1955.
White, C. Langdon, and Edwin J. Foscue. *Regional Geography of Anglo-America* (Chapter 11, The Great Plains). Prentice-Hall, Inc., 1954.
Wilson, Charles Morrow. *Grass and People.* University of Florida Press, 1961.

DESERT

Berrill, Jacquelyn. *Wonders of the Woods and Desert at Night.* Dodd, Mead & Co., 1963.
Carr, William H. *Desert Parade.* Viking Press, 1947.
Epstein, Sam and Beryl. *All About the Desert.* Random House, Inc., 1957.
Howes, Paul G. *The Giant Cactus Forest and Its World.* Duell, Sloan & Pearce, Inc., 1959.
Jaeger, Edmond C. *Desert Wildlife.* Stanford University Press, 1961.
—— *The North American Deserts.* Stanford University Press, 1957.

Krutch, Joseph Wood. *The Desert Year.* William Sloane Associates, 1952.
Leopold, A. Starker, and the Editors of *Life. The Desert.* Life Nature Library, Time, Inc., 1961.
Pond, Alonzo. *The Desert World.* Thomas Nelson & Sons, 1962.
Welles, Philip. *Meet the Southwest Deserts.* Dale Stuart King, Pub., 1960.
Werner, Jane, and the Staff of the Walt Disney Studio. *Walt Disney's Living Desert.* Simon and Schuster, Inc., 1954.

FOREST

Braun, E. Lucy. *Deciduous Forests of Eastern North America.* Blakiston, 1950.
Collingwood, G. H., and Warren D. Brush. *Knowing Your Trees.* American Forestry Association, 1964 edition.
Farb, Peter. *Face of North America* (Chapter 5, The Forests). Harper & Row, 1963.
Farb, Peter, and the Editors of *Life. The Forest.* Time, Inc., 1961.
Grimm, William Carey. *The Book of Trees.* The Stackpole Co., 1957.
Lillard, Richard G. *The Great Forest.* Alfred A. Knopf, Inc., 1947.
McCormick, Jack. *The Living Forest.* Harper and Brothers, 1959.
Neal, Ernest. *Woodland Ecology.* Harvard University Press, 1958.
Platt, Rutherford. *1001 Questions Answered About Trees.* Dodd, Mead & Co., 1959.
Symonds, George W. D. *The Tree Identification Book.* M. Barrows & Co., 1958.

PICTURE CREDITS

The publisher gratefully acknowledges:

American Museum of Natural History for the photographs on pages: 18, 20–21, 24, 34, 35, 36, 37, 38, 39, 40, 43, 48, 49, 50, 51, 52.

Buffalo Museum of Science for the photograph on page 86.

Carnegie Institute of Washington for the photograph on page 29.

Dr. Leigh E. Chadwick for the photograph on page 173.

Lynwood M. Chace for the photographs on pages: 70, 89 (top), 148 (top), 152, 170.

National Wildlife Federation for the photographs on pages: 53, 76 (painting by Roger Tory Peterson), 177 (painting by Roger Tory Peterson).

New Mexico Department of Development for the photograph on page 108.

New Mexico State Tourist Bureau for the photograph on page 111.

Science Service for the photographs on pages: 12, 66, 73, 92, 166, 169, 173, 174.

Smithsonian Institution for the photograph on page 31.

United States Department of Agriculture for the photographs on pages: 82, 84 (top right), 104, 110, 125.
Forest Service for the photographs on pages: 74, 130, 133, 134, 135, 138, 141, 142, 143, 144.
Soil Conservation Service for the photographs on pages 84 (top left) and 85.

United States Department of the Interior
Bureau of Land Management for the photograph on page 107.
Bureau of Reclamation for the photographs on pages: 96, 100, 103, 105, 114, 119.
Fish and Wildlife Service for the photographs on pages: 41, 42, 44, 45, 47, 54, 64, 67, 69, 75 (painting by Louis-Agassiz Fuertes), 78, 87, 89 (bottom), 93, 95, 115 120, 122, 123, 124, 128, 147, 148 (bottom), 149, 153, 154, 156, 157, 159, 178–179.
National Park Service for the photographs on pages: 56, 63, 68.

Phil Walters for the photograph on page 168.